GRADE 5

California Treasures

W9-BZA-686

Practice
Book

Macmillan/McGraw-Hill

The McGraw-Hill Companies

 Macmillan
McGraw-Hill

Published by Macmillan/McGraw-Hill, of McGraw-Hill Education, a division of The McGraw-Hill Companies, Inc.,
Two Penn Plaza, New York, New York 10121.

Printed in the United States of America

10 11 12 13 14   RHR 15 14 13

Contents

Unit 1 • Taking a Stand

Contents

Unit 2 • The American West

Contents

Unit 3 • Using Your Wits

Contents

Unit 4 • Team Up to Survive

© Macmillan/McGraw-Hill

Contents

Unit 5 • Investigations

Contents

Unit 6 • Changes

Overcoming Obstacles
Miss Alaineous

Growing Up
Carlos and the Skunk

Changing Lives
A Dream Comes True

Fitting In
Weslandia

Taking a Chance
The Gri Gri Tree

© Macmillan/McGraw-Hill

Name _____ Chav :) _____

The letters **a**, **e**, **i**, **o**, and **u** usually stand for the short vowel sounds /a/ in **damp**, /e/ in **ten**, /i/ in **sit**, /o/ in **hop**, and /u/ in **fun**. Some words with short vowel sounds do not follow this pattern. For example, **ea**, as in **head**, can have the /e/ sound, and **ou** followed by **gh**, as in **rough**, can have the /u/ sound.

Place each word in the column that describes the short vowel sound found in the word.

batch	rough	stump	jut	tenth
love	myth	nick	sense	cot
bread	notch	scan	tough	damp
lot	stamp	sick	fence	rhythm

short **a**	short **e**	short **i**	short **o**	short **u**
batch	bread	myth	love	stump
stamp	sense	nick	lot	jut
scan	fence	sick	rough	
damp	tenth	rhythm	notch	
			tough	
			cot	

Name _____

A. Match the vocabulary word with its definition. Then write the correct word on the line.

blurted	permission	scald	autograph
fare	spectacular	clenched	approached

1. sensational, fantastic _____spectacular_____

2. burn _____blurted_____

3. spoke suddenly _____approached_____

4. came near _____scald_____

5. closed together tightly _____clenched_____

6. consent _____Fare_____

7. a person's signed name _____permission_____

8. price charged for public transportation _____autograph_____

B. Write a paragraph using at least three vocabulary words. Underline each vocabulary word you use.

I have a picnic at winter night. I was blurter the firecame, then I was warm, then I wan't be sleeping. wen't sleep my mom and Dad sleep too. went I am wake up mom and dad already drive home then I am in the car.

 CA R 1.0 Word Analysis, Fluency, and Systematic Vocabulary Development

© Macmillan/McGraw-Hill

Name _____ Chau ___ Room 20 _____

When you summarize a story, you briefly retell it in your own words. You can describe the **characters** (people in the story), **setting** (place where the story happens), and plot development in a summary.

Read this story, and then summarize it. Include information about the characters, setting, and development of the plot.

'Tricia Ann listened carefully to her grandmother, Mama Frances. Everyone listened carefully to Mama Frances because the old woman was wise, strong, and had a no-nonsense attitude. She also had a huge heart.

" 'Tricia Ann," Mama Frances said, "it's your first trip alone downtown. Don't let anyone give you what-for, you hear? You keep going to Someplace Special with your head held high." Mama Frances was determined to boost her granddaughter's pride and self-confidence.

'Tricia Ann walked through the city. She saw sign after sign proclaiming Whites Only and Colored Section. White people glared at her as she passed them on the sidewalk. She wanted to run home crying. But 'Tricia Ann held her head high and walked bravely through the city streets.

Finally, she was there! 'Tricia Ann climbed the steps to the public library, her very own special place, where everyone was welcome. She knew that Mama Frances was right: March proudly, and you will get to where you want to go.

Summary: _Tricia Ann listened carefuly to her grandmother, Mama Frances. Everyone listened carefully to her because old woman was wise strong, and had no-nonsense attiude. The she had a heart._

Name _____

As you read *Goin' Someplace Special*, fill in the Character and Setting Chart.

Character	Setting

How does the information you wrote in the Character and Setting Chart help you analyze the story structure of *Goin' Someplace Special*?

 CA   R 2.0 Reading Comprehension (Focus on Informational Materials)

Name _____

As I read, I will pay attention to my expression.

	Josie and Franklin had heard Gramma's stories many
8	times, but they never got tired of them. There was something
19	so comforting about Gramma's voice. Josie felt as if she were
30	being wrapped in a warm, fuzzy blanket when she listened to
41	Gramma's stories. And even though Franklin was 14 going
49	on 15, he still liked to hear Gramma's stories about her life in
61	the South.
63	Now Franklin got up from the step where he had been
74	sitting. "Gramma, I have to go do my math homework. I'll
85	see you at dinner."
89	Josie stayed where she was. Like Gramma, Josie loved
98	nature, but living in the city didn't provide much. She looked
109	around the neighborhood. Outside their second-floor
115	apartment, Gramma had planted window boxes, bright with
123	red and white geraniums. Other than that, a few spindly trees
134	that grew between the sidewalk and the curb were the only
145	green, growing things that Josie could see.
152	Other neighbors were sitting on their front stoops, too,
161	hoping for a cool evening breeze. 167

Comprehension Check

1. Why does Josie enjoy listening to Gramma's stories? **Plot Development**

2. What do Josie and her grandmother have in common? **Main Idea and Details**

	Words Read	−	Number of Errors	=	Words Correct Score
First Read		−		=	
Second Read		−		=	

© Macmillan/McGraw-Hill

R 1.1 Read aloud narrative and expository text fluently and accurately and with appropriate pacing, intonation, and expression.

Name _____

A **time line** is a diagram that organizes information. Time lines help you keep track of events in the order in which they took place.

Look at the time line. Then answer the questions.

Important Civil Rights Dates

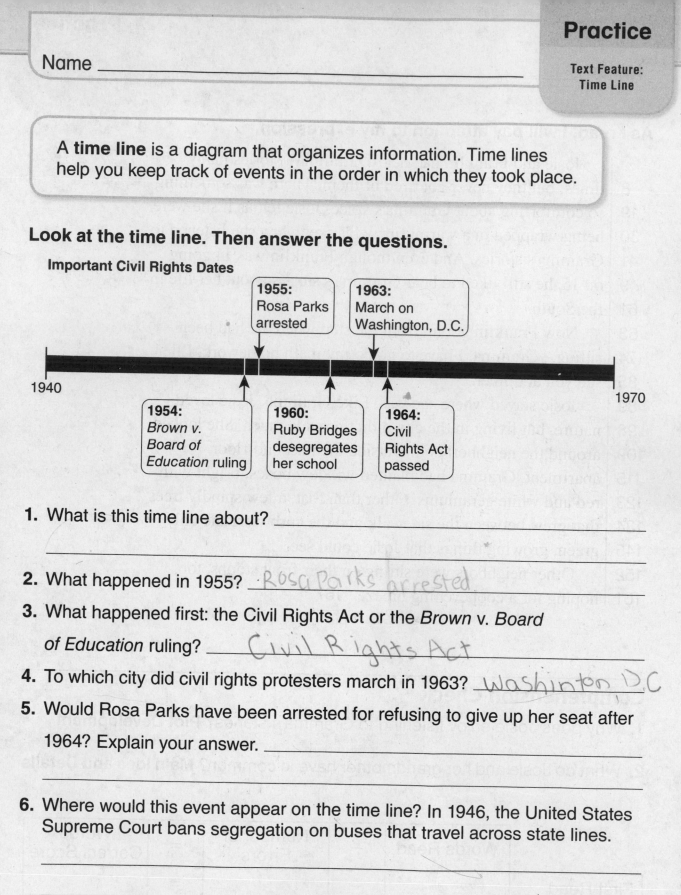

1955:
Rosa Parks
arrested

1963:
March on
Washington, D.C.

1940 — 1970

1954:
*Brown v.
Board of
Education* ruling

1960:
Ruby Bridges
desegregates
her school

1964:
Civil
Rights Act
passed

1. What is this time line about? _____

_____

2. What happened in 1955? _Rosa Parks arrested_

3. What happened first: the Civil Rights Act or the *Brown* v. *Board of Education* ruling? _Civil Rights Act_

4. To which city did civil rights protesters march in 1963? _Washinton D.C_

5. Would Rosa Parks have been arrested for refusing to give up her seat after 1964? Explain your answer. _____

_____

6. Where would this event appear on the time line? In 1946, the United States Supreme Court bans segregation on buses that travel across state lines.

_____

_____

 CA   **R 2.1** Understand how text features (e.g., format, graphics, sequence, diagrams, illustrations, charts, maps) make information accessible and usable.

Name _Chau_

Homophones are words that sound the same but have different spellings and different meanings. Sometimes you need to read the words around a homophone to know which spelling and meaning makes the most sense.

A. Write the word from the box that best completes each sentence.

fair	their	way	bored
fare	there	weigh	board

Grandma always gives me bus ____their____ to go downtown. I ____fare____ the bus and sit in the last seat. It isn't ____way____ that I have to sit in the back, but I'm never _____. I watch people carry _____ packages. Those bundles must _____ so much! I ride the bus all the _____ to the library. I'm so happy when I'm _____.

B. Circle the two homophones in each sentence. Then answer the question.

1. The wind blew my blue hat away.

   Which word refers to a color? _____

2. I had to write the right word for each item on the test.

   Which word means "correct"? _____

3. Marta took one more turn and won the spelling bee.

   Which word means that someone has gained victory? _____

4. It is great to live in our state's capital because we can visit the capitol any time.

   Which word refers to a building? _____

Name _____

Using the Word Study Steps

1. LOOK at the word.
2. SAY the word aloud.
3. STUDY the letters in the word.
4. WRITE the word.
5. CHECK the word.
   Did you spell the word right?
   If not, go back to step 1.

A. Find and Circle

Where are the spelling words?

d a m p e f g t e n t h w r t a r l t q g u e s s t u c o t z r	
b r d s t u m p e l a u g h b z x e n i c k a r t s h r u g e t	
s c a n t o u g h m t s a p b a t c h e y s e n s e g l u w a	
g f l i n g i g u s h r o u g h h j u t a h c s t u f f d o v e	
c k o d h w q l e a d v n o t c h c n i h c l o k m l p u e r	

B. Alphabetical Order

Use the lines below to write the spelling words in alphabetical order.

1. tenth   6. _____   11. _____   16. _____
2. guess   7. _____   12. _____   17. _____
3. damp   8. _____   13. _____   18. _____
4. cot   9. _____   14. _____   19. _____
5. laugh   10. _____   15. _____   20. _____

 CA **LC 1.5** Spell roots, suffixes, prefixes, contractions, and syllable constructions correctly.

Name _____ Chau _____

A. Circle the misspelled words in the set of instructions. Write the words correctly on the lines below.

You will receive a list of ten words for the spelling bee. Before the contest begins, skain the list of words. The tinth word on the list is a bonus word. Its spelling is unusual and may stumpe you. You will get an extra point if you spell the bonus word correctly.

Here are some tips for the contest. If a word does not make cents to you, ask to hear it again. If you are not sure how to spell a word, take a gess. Last but not least, don't worry if your hands feel dap. That just means you are feeling a little nervous.

1. _____   3. _____   5. _____

2. _____   4. _____   6. _____

B. Writing Activity

Have you ever watched or taken part in a contest? Write a description of what happened or what you think might happen at a contest, using four spelling words.

_____

_____

_____

_____

_____

_____

_____

_____

_____

CA **LC 1.5** Spell roots, suffixes, prefixes, contractions, and syllable constructions correctly.

Name _____

> • A **command** tells someone to do something. It ends with a period.
> • An **exclamation** expresses strong feeling. It ends with an exclamation point.

Read each sentence. Decide whether each sentence is a command or an exclamation, and write your choice on the line. Then rewrite the sentence with the correct end mark.

1. Please tell me what the vocabulary words are for this week

_____

_____

2. Write each word five times

_____

3. Be sure to include each word's definition

_____

4. Oh my, she hung up the phone with a crash

_____

_____

5. Line up by the board for the Vocabulary Parade

_____

_____

6. How sad for Sage to feel so devastated

_____

_____

7. Wow, that's an amazing gold trophy that Sage won

_____

_____

8. Oh no, Mr. Bell's suit is all soggy

_____

CA LC 1.0 Written and Oral English Language Conventions

© Macmillan/McGraw-Hill

Name _____ Chav _____

- Begin every **sentence** with a capital letter.
- Place a period at the end of a **statement**.
- Place a question mark at the end of a **question**.
- Place a period at the end of a **command**.
- Place an exclamation point at the end of an **exclamation**.

Rewrite the paragraph below. Use the correct capitalization and punctuation marks.

I like spelling? it's my favorite subject! Each week, our teacher gives us 20 spelling words? I always write the words in my notebook! the boy who sits next to me sneezed? How sick I became. I could not be at school the day our teacher gave us the spelling words? I called my friend to get the words for the week? I feel confident that I will get all the words right on the test! this is going to be easy? i hope i'm not sick the day of the spelling test!

I Like spelling! It's my favorite subject. Each week, our teacher gives us 20 spelling words. I alway write the words in my notebook. The boy who sits next to me is sneezed. I became sick. I could not be at school the day our teacher gave us the spelling words. I called my friend to get the words for the week. I feel confident that I will get all the words right on the test. This is going to be easy! I hope I'm not sike the day of the spelling test!

Name _____

Make a list of 5 things that happened in your day today:

Example: Got wet in the rain

_____

_____

_____

_____

_____

_____

_____

Pick one of these moments and write 5 sentences about that moment ONLY.

Example: I had just rounded the corner and could see my school in the distance when suddenly the sky turned black. A threatening mass of clouds obscured the sun and rain started pouring down. I held my backpack over my head and sprinted for the building. Unfortunately, I wasn't fast enough to escape the rain and by the time I got to the front door I was soaked from head to toe. My math homework was ruined and I had to wear wet socks all day.

_____

_____

_____

_____

_____

_____

_____

_____

 W 1.0 Writing Strategies

Name _____

Words that have the VCe pattern usually have a **long vowel** sound, as in *fame*, *mine*, and *bone*. The vowel digraphs *ai* and *ay* usually stand for the long *a* sound, as in *pail* and *play*. The digraphs *ee* and *ea* stand for the long *e* sound, as in *see* and *heap*. The digraphs *oa* and *ow* can stand for the long *o* sound, as in *boat* and *flow*. The vowel *i* can stand for the long *i* sound in words such as *wind* and *wild*. The letters *igh* in *high* can also stand for the long *i* sound.

A. Write the words from the box that have the same long vowel sound as the first word in each row. Underline the letters that make the long vowel sound.

| coach | bike | wheat | pain | may | deep |
| steam | flight | slate | towing | mind | float |

1. rake _____bike_____ _____may_____ _____slate_____

2. feet _____deep_____ _____steam_____ _____wheat_____

3. kite _____mind_____ _____flight_____ _____pain_____

4. flow _____towing_____ _____float_____ _____coach_____

B. Write a sentence using as many long vowel sound words as possible.

_____I use a bike to go to school._____

_____

_____

© Macmillan/McGraw-Hill

Name _____

A. Use the correct word from the list to complete each sentence.

> injury   mournful   sympathy   delivering
> couple   shrieks   decency

1. The mother felt ___sympathy___ toward the hawk.

2. Did you hear the ___shrieks___ of all those birds?

3. I saw them ___delivering___ the hawk to the veterinarian.

4. The hawk had suffered an ___injury___ but was going to survive.

5. The mother and child had the ___decency___ to stop the car and take care of the hawk.

6. People can become very ___mournful___ when they see injured animals.

7. I hope the bird will get well in a ___couple___ of days.

B. Use the vocabulary words to answer the questions.

8. **shrieks** What do shrieks sound like?

___shrieks sound like a loud sound___
_____

9. **mournful** What does it mean to be mournful?

___feeling or epressing sorrow or grief___
_____

10. **decency** What are some ways people show decency?

_____
_____

 R 1.0 Word Analysis, Fluency, and Systematic Vocabulary Development

Name _____ Chau _____

Making inferences can help you trace the **plot development** of a story. To make inferences, use story clues and your own knowledge. Then you make a logical decision about story events not directly stated in the text, but that contribute to the development of the plot.

Read the selection. Then make inferences to answer the questions.

Maria walked into the kitchen with a frown on her face. Her mother was standing over the counter, chopping red peppers. Maria sat down on a small stool.

Maria's mother looked up from her cutting board. "Maria, you need to cheer up. Rowdy wasn't your dog. It's not fair for you to keep him."

"I know," Maria began. "I'll be all right. I'll just miss when Rowdy jumps on my belly when I'm lying on the floor. I'll miss when he curls up in that shoe box. I'll just miss him."

Maria's mother stopped chopping and walked over beside her daughter. "Sweetie, don't you worry. Your birthday is right around the corner, and I know just what to get you."

Maria's face lit up. "Oh, Mom!" she exclaimed, hugging her mother.

1. How is Maria feeling in the beginning of the story? How do you know?

She feeling worries because she frown on her face

2. How is Maria feeling at the end of the story? How do you know?

She feeling good because her face lit up

3. How big is Rowdy? How do you know?

it was big

4. What do you think will happen on Maria's birthday?

Her birthday wrigh around the corner.

CA **R 2.4** Draw **inferences**, conclusions, or generalizations about text and support them with textual evidence and prior knowledge.

Shiloh • Grade 5/Unit I   **23**

© Macmillan/McGraw-Hill

Name _____

As you read *Shiloh*, fill in the Inferences Chart.

Plot Clues	What You Know	Inferences

How does the information you wrote in this Inferences Chart help you monitor comprehension of *Shiloh*?

 R 2.4 Draw **inferences**, conclusions, or generalizations about text and support them with textual evidence and prior knowledge.

Name _____

As I read, I will pay attention to my intonation.

	Just past the admissions window, not far from a display of
11	llamas, Mrs. Battaglia assembled her students. She blew her
20	nose, cleared her throat, and said, "There are ten endangered
30	animals here at the zoo. *Achoo!*"
36	"Bless you," someone muttered.
40	"Thank you. In groups of three, you are to visit them and
52	answer all of the questions on your worksheet."
60	Alice noticed that Mrs. Battaglia's eyes were red and
69	tearing. She glanced at Wendy, who giggled. For all her talk
80	about their fascinating blood cells, Mrs. Battaglia was clearly
89	too allergic to go anywhere near actual animals.
97	"At the end of today, your group will choose one—*achoo!*—
108	animal. It will be your assignment to find a way to raise
120	money for that animal at the school fundraiser in two weeks."
131	Wendy grabbed Alice's hand. "Let's go together," she
139	said. 140

Comprehension Check

1. What does *allergic* mean in this passage? **Context Clues**

2. How do you think Mrs. Battaglia feels about the field trip to the zoo?
Plot Development

	Words Read	–	Number of Errors	=	Words Correct Score
First Read		–		=	
Second Read		–		=	

R 1.1 Read aloud narrative and expository text fluently and accurately
and with appropriate pacing, **intonation**, and expression.

Name _____

> A **photograph** can help you see what a story or article is explaining or describing. The photograph's **caption** provides more information about what you see in the photograph.

Look at the photograph, read the caption, and then put a check next to the statements that would be included in the article.

People come to choose and adopt animals at the animal shelter.

1. ✓_____ Ten dogs, five cats, seven kittens, and twelve puppies were adopted in all.

2. _____ The Lions Club will be holding their annual fair from July 30 through August 4.

3. _____ There was a clown giving out balloons and a cowboy offering free pony rides.

4. _____ There was an Adoption Fair at the Third Street animal shelter today.

5. _____✓ Eleven-year-old Richard Vitarelli went home with a beagle pup.

6. _____✓ People were encouraged to take prospective pets out of their crates and get acquainted with the animals.

CA **R 2.1** Understand how text features (e.g., format, graphics, sequence, diagrams, **illustrations**, charts, maps) make information accessible and usable.

Name _____

- Be sure that every sentence begins with a **capital letter** and ends with the correct **punctuation mark**.
- Use commas to separate three or more words or phrases in a series.
- When combining subjects and predicates, use the words *and* or *or*.

Rewrite the passage, combining sentences and adding commas where needed. Use correct capitalization and punctuation.

davy Crockett was a frontiersman. He chopped wood hunted wild animals and ran a powder mill. Every morning, he got up early to see the sunrise. He got up early to eat breakfast.

one day, Sally Sugartree asked Davy to dance. Davy wouldn't dance because his boots were too big. He wouldn't dance because he would step on her toes. sally then asked Davy to sing. His voice was so strong that it made the trees sway the clouds move and the animals scatter. Sally liked Davy's voice so much that she decided to marry him.

Davy Crockett was frontiersman. He chopped wood hunted wild animals and ran a power milles. Everymorning, he got up early to see the sunrise. He got up early to eat break fast. One day, Sally Sugartree asked Davy to dance. Davy wouldn't dance because his boots were too big. He wouldn't dance Because he would step on her toes. Sally then asked Davy to sing. His voice wasso strong that it made the trees away the clouds move the animals scatter. Sally liked Davy's voice so much the she decide to marry him.

© Macmillan/McGraw-Hill

LC 1.0 Written and Oral English Language Conventions
LC 1.4 Use correct capitalization.

Shiloh • Grade 5/Unit 1   **31**

Please read the following journal entry:

Max tried to make a lay-up. His body sprang towards the hoop. I heard the Bump! as the ball hit the backboard. But it didn't go in. I made a lay-up later on. It looked like my hand was waving goodbye to the ball as it went into the net. My whole team yelled "Yeah!"

Pick one moment from the journal entry and write 3 more showing sentences about what happened in that moment.

Example: His body sprang towards the hoop. I crossed my fingers as I watched Max's feet leave the ground. Everything seemed to be moving in slow motion. The crowd looked like a sea of eyes, and they were all on Max.

_____

_____

_____

_____

_____

_____

_____

_____

_____

_____

_____

_____

_____

_____

Name _____

Using the Word Study Steps

1. LOOK at the word.
2. SAY the word aloud.
3. STUDY the letters in the word.
4. WRITE the word.
5. CHECK the word.
   Did you spell the word right?
   If not, go back to step 1.

Find Rhyming Words

Circle the word in each row that rhymes with the word in dark type.

1. **lose**	choose	close	lost
2. **booth**	both	tooth	comb
3. **hue**	who	would	cue
4. **mute**	cute	mood	flunk
5. **duty**	sooty	fruity	dust
6. **view**	grow	shoes	few
7. **plume**	gloom	plunk	put
8. **soothe**	tow	smooth	root
9. **hooks**	moods	broke	brooks
10. **bruise**	brush	burn	cruise
11. **prove**	shove	move	dove
12. **doom**	room	dorm	dome
13. **hoof**	roof	half	woof
14. **few**	feud	stew	fool
15. **amuse**	confuse	amidst	among

© Macmillan/McGraw-Hill

LC 1.5 Spell roots, suffixes, prefixes, contractions, and syllable
constructions correctly.

Maya Lin, Architect of Memory **41**
Grade 5/Unit I

A. Circle the misspelled words in the paragraph. Write the words correctly on the lines below.

Our backyard has only a fue trees. The big maple tree is my favorite. I have a good vyoo of it from my room. All the trees in the yard are deciduous. They all loos their leaves in the fall. Before that happens, though, their leaves change color. The maple's leaves turn a red hiew. I amewz myself by collecting maple leaves each fall. Once I found a ploom from a bird on the ground by the maple. I saved it along with the leaves I had collected.

1. _____
3. _____
5. _____

2. _____
4. _____
6. _____

B. Writing Activity

Write about something in nature that interests you. Use four spelling words in your description.

_____
_____
_____
_____
_____
_____
_____
_____
_____
_____
_____
_____

 LC 1.5 Spell roots, suffixes, prefixes, contractions, and syllable constructions correctly.

Name _____

Writing Rubric			
4 Excellent	3 Good	2 Fair	1 Unsatisfactory
Ideas and Content/Genre	Ideas and Content/Genre	Ideas and Content/Genre	Ideas and Content/Genre
Organization and Focus	Organization and Focus	Organization and Focus	Organization and Focus
Sentence Structure/ Fluency	Sentence Structure/ Fluency	Sentence Structure/ Fluency	Sentence Structure/ Fluency
Conventions	Conventions	Conventions	Conventions
Word Choice	Word Choice	Word Choice	Word Choice
Voice	Voice	Voice	Voice
Presentation	Presentation	Presentation	Presentation

- The letters *ar* usually stand for the /är/ sound in *car* and *carve*.
- The letters *ear* and *are* can stand for the /âr/ sound in *bear* and *care*.
- The letters *or, ore, oar,* and *our* can stand for the /ôr/ sound in *for, core, roar,* and *your*.

A. Underline the words in the paragraph that have the /är/ sound as in *car*, the /âr/ sound as in *bear*, or the /ôr/ sound as in *for*.

The astronauts climbed aboard their spaceship. They wore spacesuits made from special fabric. Their goal was to travel far into space and explore a nearby star. During the flight, they had many chores to do. They also had to take care not to tear holes in their suits.

B. Sort the underlined words in the paragraph according to the vowel + *r* sound.

/är/ sound in *car*	/âr/ sound in *bear*	/ôr/ sound in *for*
_____	_____	_____
_____	_____	_____
_____	_____	_____
_____	_____	_____

 R 1.0 Word Analysis, Fluency, and Systematic Vocabulary Development

Name _____

As you read *The Night of San Juan*, fill in the Story Map.

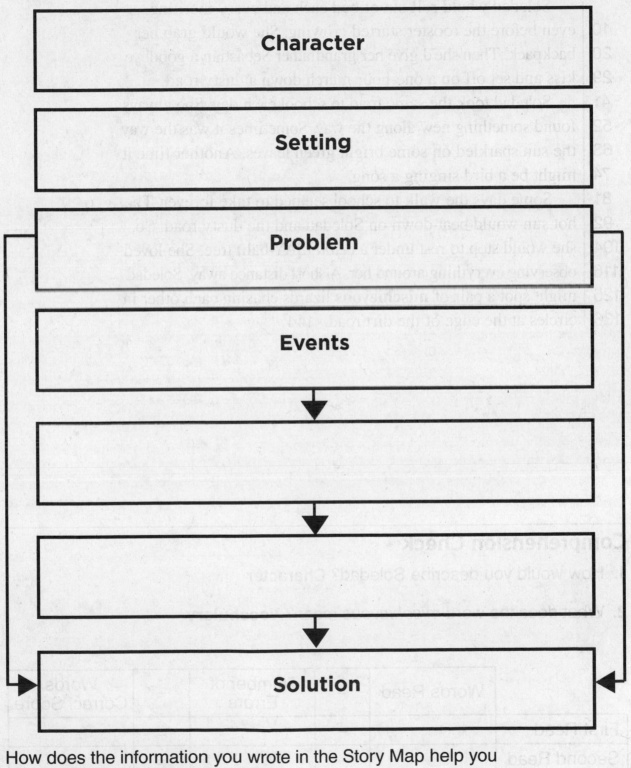

Character

Setting

Problem

Events

Solution

How does the information you wrote in the Story Map help you summarize *The Night of San Juan*?

Name _Chao_

As I read, I will pay attention to pauses and intonation.

	Soledad would roll out of bed each and every morning,
10	even before the rooster started crowing. She would grab her
20	backpack. Then she'd give her grandfather Sebastián a goodbye
29	kiss and set off on a one-hour march down a dusty road.
41	Soledad took the same road to school each day. She always
52	found something new along the way. Sometimes it was the way
63	the sun sparkled on some bright green leaves. Another time it
74	might be a bird singing a song.
81	Some days the walk to school seemed to take forever. The
92	hot sun would beat down on Soledad and the dusty road. So,
104	she would stop to rest under a *ceiba* (SAY-bah) tree. She loved
116	observing everything around her. A short distance away, Soledad
125	might spot a pair of **mischievous** lizards chasing each other in
136	circles at the edge of the dirt road. 144

Comprehension Check

1. How would you describe Soledad? **Character**

2. What does the word *mischievous* mean? **Vocabulary**

	Words Read	−	Number of Errors	=	Words Correct Score
First Read	140	−	0	=	140
Second Read	149	−	0	=	144

 CA

R 1.1 Read aloud narrative and expository text fluently and accurately
and with appropriate pacing, intonation, and expression.

Name _____

A **diagram** is a graphic aid that shows information. The important parts of the diagram are labeled. A diagram can help readers make comparisons.

Read the diagram. Then answer the questions.

Top View of Surfboard   Side View of Surfboard

Leash   Rail   Stringer
Cup   Nose   Nose   Deck   Tail
Tail   Rail
                                                        Rocker
Leash   Bottom   Fin
          Rail   Deck

1. What does the diagram show? _____

2. How is the nose of the surfboard different from the tail? _____
   _____
   _____

3. How is the side view the same and different from the top view? _____
   _____
   _____
   _____

4. Why do you think a surfboard has a leash cup? _____
   _____

5. Which part of the surfboard makes the surfboard stronger because it
   provides support in the center of the board? _____

© Macmillan/McGraw-Hill

Suffixes are word parts added to the ends of base words to change their meanings or their parts of speech.

- The suffix **-ity** means "the state of." For example, when you add the suffix **-ity** to *visible*, the word *visibility* means "the state of being visible."
- The suffix **-ion** means "act or process." When you add **-ion** to *demonstrate*, the word *demonstration* means "the act of demonstrating."
- The suffix **-ous** means "having the qualities of." For example, when you add **-ous** to the word *poison*, the word *poisonous* means "having the qualities of poison."

In each sentence, underline the word that includes the suffix -ity, -ion, or -ous. Then write each word and its meaning. Remember that there may be spelling changes when you add the suffix.

1. The mischievous girl liked to play tricks on her sisters.

   _____

2. Amalia has the ability to make friends easily.

   _____

3. With no hesitation, the boy loudly declared, "I want to go, too!"

   _____

4. Juan was suspicious of his younger brother when the last cookie disappeared.

   _____

5. Our Spanish teacher always makes us work on our pronunciation.

   _____

© Macmillan/McGraw-Hill

 R 1.0 Word Analysis, Fluency, and Systematic Vocabulary Development

Name _____

Please read the following passage:

> We all had a great time at the park during the last week of school. It wasn't fair to have to go to school into July just because of a snow day. Jamee missed three days of the last week of school.

Choose one of the sentences above and write two more sentences about that topic that will develop one theme. Remember that theme is the author's message or feeling because of the topic or events that are happening.

Example: We all had a great time at the park during the last week of school. Every day was warm and sunny, perfect for playing flag football. I was excited because my team won 3 out of 5 games and no one on the other team was a sore loser.

_____

_____

_____

_____

_____

_____

_____

_____

_____

Name _____

The letters *ur*, *er*, *ir*, and *ear* can stand for the **/ûr/** sound, as in *fur*, *her*, *bird*, and *earn*. The letters *ear* and *eer* can stand for the **/îr/** sound, as in *fear* and *deer*.

A. Place each word in the column that best represents its vowel sound.

squirm	dreary	engineer	verse	clear
nerve	lurch	learn	sneer	ear

/ûr/, as in *fur*	/îr/, as in *fear*
1. _____	6. _____
2. _____	7. _____
3. _____	8. _____
4. _____	9. _____
5. _____	10. _____

B. Answer the questions using the chart above.

11. How can the /ûr/ sound be spelled?

_____

12. How can the /îr/ sound be spelled?

_____

 R 1.0 Word Analysis, Fluency, and Systematic Vocabulary Development

Name _____

Complete each sentence by choosing the best word from the box.

inspect	navigation	patriots	tyrant
governor	stark	instruct	

1. Paul Revere and others were great American _____ who loved their country and warned the colonists of British attacks.

2. The colonists wanted to _____ the ships to make sure they were not carrying spies.

3. The _____ of the *Somerset*, a British ship, was not an easy task, especially in the dangerous seas.

4. Many American colonists believed that they were being treated cruelly

   by a _____.

5. A _____ helped keep order and enforce the laws in the American colonies.

6. The landscape was _____ on the night of Paul Revere's famous midnight ride.

Name _____

As you read, you can **draw conclusions** by thinking about text clues and what you already know. This helps you arrive at a new understanding about the **plot development** in a story.

**Read the following lines from "The Midnight Ride of Paul Revere."
Then answer the questions.**

You know the rest in the books you have read
How the British Regulars fired and fled,
How the farmers gave them ball for ball,
From behind each fence and the farmyard wall,
Chasing the red-coats down the lane,
Then crossing the fields to emerge again
Under the trees at the turn of the road,
And only pausing to fire and load.

1. What conclusion can you make about the colonists fighting the British Regulars? What evidence supports your conclusion?

   _____

   _____

   _____

   _____

2. Did the British retreat? What line(s) from the poem support your conclusion?

   _____

3. How do you know that the colonists were determined to gain their independence? What was the result of their fight for freedom?

   _____

   _____

   _____

CA R 2.4 Draw inferences, **conclusions**, or generalizations about text and support them with textual evidence and prior knowledge.

© Macmillan/McGraw-Hill

Name _____

**As you read *Sleds on Boston Common*, fill in the
Conclusions Chart.**

Text Clues	Conclusion

How does the information you wrote in the Conclusions Chart help you
make inferences and analyze *Sleds on Boston Common*?

R 2.4 Draw inferences, **conclusions**, or generalizations about text and
support them with textual evidence and prior knowledge.

As I read, I will pay attention to phrasing.

	Life in the colonies was changing. Roads had been built
10	connecting the cities. The colonies were trading with one
19	another more. People and ideas were moving along with
28	goods. These changes had made the ties among the colonists
38	stronger. They were beginning to feel more American
46	than British.
48	Then, in 1765, the British passed the Stamp Act. It was
58	one of the taxes that the British were using to help pay for
71	their war with France.
75	The colonists were furious. It wasn't only the money,
84	although times were hard. They were angry because they
93	hadn't voted for this tax. The colonists believed that only
103	representatives they chose could ask them to pay taxes.
111	The colonists said there could be "no taxation without
121	representation."
122	And so the first step toward the American Revolution
131	began over a fight about taxes.
137	Colonists refused to pay the stamp tax. Some people
146	boycotted, or refused to buy, British goods or enter any store
157	that carried British goods. 161

Comprehension Check

1. What caused the colonists to feel more American than British?
   Cause and Effect

2. Why were colonists so angry about the Stamp Act? **Main Idea and Details**

	Words Read	−	Number of Errors	=	Words Correct Score
First Read		−		=	
Second Read		−		=	

 R 1.1 Read aloud narrative and expository text fluently and accurately and with appropriate pacing, intonation, and expression.

Name _____

Narrative poetry is poetry that tells a story or gives an account of events. **Meter** is the regular arrangement of accented and unaccented syllables in a line of poetry. **Alliteration** is the repetition of the same first letter or sound in a series of words.

A. Read the passage from the poem. Mark the meter of each line by separating the syllables with a slash. Then underline the accented syllables. Then answer the questions.

> Meanwhile, his friend, through alley and street,
> Wanders and watches, with eager ears,
> Till in the silence around him he hears
> The muster of men at the barrack door,
> And the measured tread of the grenadiers,
> Marching down to their boats on the shore.

1. Based on this passage, how do you know the poem is narrative poetry?

   _____

   _____

   _____

2. Which lines use alliteration? Give examples.

   _____

   _____

   _____

B. Rewrite the following line so that it uses alliteration.

3. Marching down to their boats on the shore.

   _____

Name _____

Many long words have smaller base words within them. With
many words it is easy to build **word families** by adding
a **suffix** or a **prefix** to a base word.

**A. For the words listed below, write an additional word that belongs
to the same word family.**

1. patriot

unpatriotic _____

2. tyrant

tyrannical _____

3. navigate

navigation _____

4. govern

governor _____

**B. Complete the sentence by using the correct word from the word
families above.**

5. The American colonists created their own _____.

6. A person who is not loyal to his or her country is said to be

_____.

7. Paul Revere showed great _____ for the American colonies
during his midnight ride.

8. The _____ of the *Somerset*, a British ship, had to have
good eyesight.

© Macmillan/McGraw-Hill

 R 1.0 Word Analysis, Fluency, and Systematic Vocabulary Development

Name _____

1. Please review the following chart. In the first column is a list of themes. In the second column is text from some journal entries.

Theme	Textual Evidence	Relevant/Not Relevant
Problem Solving	"Now all I needed was some peace and quiet."	
Problem Solving	"Luckily, I got an idea! I wrapped my makeshift pillow around my head. It worked perfectly, almost drowning out all of the sound."	
Being Prepared	"Bug spray—check, sleeping bag—check, pillow—check."	
Being Prepared	"Unfortunately, what I received was quite the opposite: laughing, sighing, hitting, and a bunch of snoring."	

2. Decide whether or not you think that the journal entry text is relevant to the theme listed next to it. Remember, relevant means related and important.

3. Depending on what you decide, write "Relevant" or "Not Relevant" in the column on the far right.

© Macmillan/McGraw-Hill

Name _____

- The **/ô/** sound can be spelled **aw**, as in **law**, **au**, as in **haul**, **ough**, as in **bought** or **augh**, as in **taught**.

- The **/ou/** sound can be spelled **ou**, as in **counter**, or **ow**, as in **cow**.

- The **/oi/** sound can be spelled **oi**, as in **boil**, or **oy**, as in **loyal**.

Write the words below in the correct column according to their vowel sounds. Remember that different letters can make the same vowel sounds. Circle the letters in each word that make the /ô/, /ou/, or /oi/ vowel sound.

dawdle	brought	crowd	toil	sought
joint	loyal	noise	mountain	loud
daughter	fountain	sprawls	foil	point
house	thought	bawl	royal	town

/ô/ sound, as in *law*	/ou/ sound, as in *now*	/oi/ sound, as in *boy*
1. _____	1. _____	1. _____
2. _____	2. _____	2. _____
3. _____	3. _____	3. _____
4. _____	4. _____	4. _____
5. _____	5. _____	5. _____
6. _____	6. _____	6. _____
7. _____	7. _____	7. _____

© Macmillan/McGraw-Hill

R 1.0 Word Analysis, Fluency, and Systematic Vocabulary Development

Name _____

Complete each sentence by choosing the best word from the box.

eldest	depicts	detested	ignored
refuge	projects	obvious	obedience

1. Sir Francis Drake, the first English explorer to reach California, was the _____ of 12 sons.

2. Drake went to sea as a young man, and it was soon _____ that he would be a great sailor.

3. Drake and the other sailors spent long days doing _____ on their ship.

4. Sailing across the sea was very dangerous, but sailors _____ gloomy warnings.

5. When they were caught in storms, sailors found _____ on quiet islands.

6. A painting _____ Drake meeting with Native Americans in California.

7. Some explorers from Spain _____ Drake and his crew, claiming that the English stole money from them.

8. Drake is remembered for his bravery and for his _____ to Queen Elizabeth I.

Name _____

As you read a story, look for **cause-and-effect** relationships.
A **cause** is a reason that something happens. An **effect** is the
result of the cause. For example, if settlers in an area use up one
source of food, they will look for another source. The first event
(using up one source of food) is the cause, and the second event
(looking for a new source) is the effect.

Writers use signal words and phrases such as *because*, *so*, *as a
result*, and *then* to show cause-and-effect relationships.

**Read the following article. Circle the signal words that show cause-
and-effect relationships. Then, on the lines below, write four pairs
of causes and effects.**

About 13,000 years ago, hunters from the north came to the area that is
now California so they could hunt the large animals that lived there. After a
while, the animals died out and then the people could not find enough food to
eat. Because they were hungry, the people started to raise crops. As a result,
they started living in villages.

1. cause _____

effect _____

2. cause _____

effect _____

3. cause _____

effect _____

4. cause _____

effect _____

© Macmillan/McGraw-Hill

 R 2.0 Reading Comprehension (Focus on Informational Materials)

Name _____

As you read *Valley of the Moon: The Diary of María Rosalia de Milagros*, fill in the Cause and Effect Chart.

Cause ➡	Effect
➡	
➡	
➡	
➡	
➡	

How does the information you wrote in this Cause and Effect Chart help you be more aware of cause-and-effect relationships as you read *Valley of the Moon: The Diary of María Rosalia de Milagros*?

CA **R 2.0** Reading Comprehension (Focus on Informational Materials)

As I read, I will pay attention to my expression.

	I handed in my Jupiter report today, but I don't remember
11	anything about the planet. That's because as soon as I got
22	home, excitement ruled. I could hear the noise about half a
33	mile away. When I got to the farm, there was bedlam!
44	"Well, if you didn't plant it, then how did it get here?"
56	I heard my mother yelling. My father said he didn't know how
68	the peculiar plant got there but that it had to be gotten rid of
82	right away. He didn't want our crop to be spoiled by some
94	mystery fruit.
96	"Hey, what's going on?" I asked over all the commotion.
106	"This!" shouted my mother as she pointed to a strange tree
117	in the middle of the orchard.
123	At first glance, when I looked at the tree, it looked like all
136	the other trees. But then I noticed the extraordinary fruit. Each
147	piece was round and yellow and had a big red spot on it. There
161	was just one spot and each piece of fruit was the same. 173

Comprehension Check

1. What is the problem? **Problem and Solution**

2. Why does the father plan to get rid of the tree? **Main Idea and Details**

	Words Read	–	Number of Errors	=	Words Correct Score
First Read		–		=	
Second Read		–		=	

© Macmillan/McGraw-Hill

 CA R 1.1 Read aloud narrative and expository text fluently and accurately and with appropriate pacing, intonation, and expression.

Name _____

> When an author wants to help a reader see and remember a sequence of events, he or she will often include a **time line**. On a **time line**, events are shown in the order in which they took place.

Use the time line below to answer the questions.

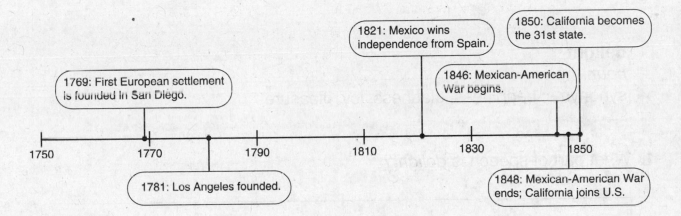

1. Which is the first event shown on the time line?

_____

2. When did Mexico win independence from Spain?

_____

3. When did the Mexican-American War begin?

_____

4. About how long did the Mexican-American War last?

_____

5. When did California become a state?

_____

R 2.1 Understand how text features (e.g., format, graphics, **sequence**, diagrams, illustrations, charts, maps) make information accessible and usable.

Valley of the Moon • Grade 5/Unit 2   **75**

Name _____

A **thesaurus** is a dictionary of **synonyms**, words that have almost the same meaning. If you are looking for just the right word, a thesaurus can help you find it.

Read this thesaurus entry. Then answer the questions below.

delight
noun
synonyms: happiness, gladness, joy, pleasure

1. What part of speech is *delight*?

   _____

2. What is another word that has almost the same meaning as *delight*?

   _____

3. Use the word *delight* in a sentence.

   _____

4. Write the sentence again, this time using a synonym for *delight*.

   _____

5. How would you find another word that means almost the same as *explore*?

   _____

 R 1.3 Understand and explain frequently used **synonyms**, antonyms, and homographs.

Name _____

Using the Word Study Steps

1. LOOK at the word.

2. SAY the word aloud.

3. STUDY the letters in the word.

4. WRITE the word.

5. CHECK the word.
   Did you spell the word right?
   If not, go back to step 1.

Here and There

Circle the spelling words in this puzzle. Each word appears once.

```
B  J  F  O  U  N  D  A  T  I  O  N  F
R  M  O  U  T  H  F  U  L  N  M  R  O
O  L  U  T  U  R  Q  U  O  I  S  E  U
U  K  L  X  B  A  W  L  P  R  T  Q  N
G  J  C  A  U  T  I  O  U  S  O  B  T
H  O  I  S  T  W  E  R  T  B  U  H  A
T  I  C  P  U  H  X  D  H  A  T  Y  I
D  N  L  R  R  S  P  R  A  W  L  S  N
O  T  A  O  M  B  C  O  I  L  V  Z  G
U  A  U  U  O  C  O  U  N  T  E  R  H
S  B  S  T  I  N  S  C  R  A  W  N  Y
E  R  E  S  L  V  D  A  W  D  L  E  C
```

 LC 1.5 Spell roots, suffixes, prefixes, contractions, and syllable constructions correctly.

Valley of the Moon • Grade 5/Unit 2   **77**

Name _____

A. Circle the misspelled words in this paragraph. Write the words correctly on the lines below.

Lupe loved to work in her island garden. She checked it every morning, looking for sprowts of vegetables and flowers. First she would douwse the plants with water. Then she sampled a mouthful of fresh tomatoes. She broght fresh flowers in and put them on the kitchen counter. Her grandmother taught her to take long-stemmed flowers and coyle them into a crown. Sometimes it was fun to daudle in the garden, and enjoy the sound of water in the fauntain.

1. _____   3. _____   5. _____

2. _____   4. _____   6. _____

B. Writing Activity

Can you imagine a beautiful park? Write a description of the park and what you might do there. Use four spelling words in your description.

_____

_____

_____

_____

_____

_____

_____

_____

_____

_____

_____

© Macmillan/McGraw-Hill

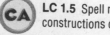 **LC 1.5** Spell roots, suffixes, prefixes, contractions, and syllable constructions correctly.

Name _____

> - A **proper noun** names a particular person, place, or thing.
> - Some **proper nouns** contain more than one word.
> - Days of the week, months of the year, and holidays are **proper nouns**.
> - A person's title is a **proper noun.**

Read each sentence. Then write it correctly on the line.

1. jonah and sally ann live in the state of california.

   _____

2. jonah hopes that dad will go to see dr. mason.

   _____

3. jonah thinks that he can earn money by delivering papers on fridays.

   _____

4. If jonah finds work in town, he can pay mr. dennis.

   _____

5. jonah looks for work in sacramento, california.

   _____

6. sally ann brushes daisy with an old hairbrush.

   _____

7. Even mrs. snow said nice things about daisy.

   _____

8. jonah asks doc mason about delivering newspapers.

   _____

9. jonah's father's name is john henry.

   _____

10. By april, jonah, sally ann, and daisy are good friends.

   _____

 LC 1.4 Use correct capitalization.

Name _____

- Capitalize every **proper noun**.
- Capitalize important words in **proper nouns** with more than one word.
- Capitalize **common nouns** only when they begin a sentence.

Circle capitalization mistakes. Then rewrite the passage correctly.

harry peters takes home a runaway Dog. It seems to harry as though the dog has been mistreated by his Owner, jack willson. mr.willson has the reputation of being mean and nasty.

mr. and mrs. peters, Harry's Parents, know that their son has grown fond of the dog, whom he has named shaggy. harry takes the dog to the Animal Doctor, dr. nickels. jack willson is angry when he finds out that the Dog has been injured. mr. peters says that his son will pay for the Animal Doctor.

_____

_____

_____

_____

_____

_____

_____

_____

_____

_____

 LC 1.4 Use correct capitalization.

© Macmillan/McGraw-Hill

Name _____

1. **Please read the following sentence:**

   William was really nervous.

2. **List five ways that you can tell when someone feels nervous.**

   a. Stuttering

   b. Biting nails

   c. Tapping pencil on desk

   d. Looking around room

   e. Fidgeting in chair

3. **Write three sentences that show the reader what William looks like and how he acted when he felt nervous:**

   William shifted nervously in his chair, biting the nails on his left hand and tapping his pencil on his desk with his right, hoping that the teacher would call on anyone but him. "This is just my luck," William thought to himself as Mr. White pointed to him to answer. "I-I-I d-d-didn't do the assignment," William stammered quickly.

Extra Practice: Write three sentences that show how Jessica looks and how she acts when she is angry.

   Jessica felt angry.

Add the letter **s** to most words to make them plural. Add **-es** to words that end in **s**, **x**, **z**, **ch**, or **sh** to form plurals. For example, **bunch** becomes **bunches**. When a word ends in the letter **y** and has a consonant before the **y**, change the **y** to **i** and then add **-es**. For example, the plural form of **bunny** is **bunnies**.

A. Write the plural form of each word on the line provided.

1. risk _____

2. century _____

3. compass _____

4. ability _____

5. rattler _____

6. loss _____

7. academy _____

8. tax _____

B. Look at each plural word below. Then write the singular form of the word on the line provided.

9. tongues _____

10. pouches _____

11. babies _____

12. forests _____

13. stories _____

14. branches _____

15. dictionaries _____

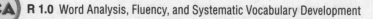

CA R 1.0 Word Analysis, Fluency, and Systematic Vocabulary Development

© Macmillan/McGraw-Hill

Name _____

Choose the correct word that best completes the following sentences. Then write a new sentence with the word.

1. Our teacher tries to (instill/insert) a love of reading in each of us.

_____

_____

_____

2. A (botanist/naturalist) is a person who studies nature. _____

_____

_____

3. The (singular/diverse) life in the park included many types of trees and wildlife.

_____

_____

_____

4. We planted a neighborhood garden in the (busy/vacant) lot.

_____

_____

_____

5. We (separated/combined) the soil with sand to help it drain well.

_____

_____

_____

A **cause** is the reason why something happens, and an **effect** is the result, or the thing that happens.

Match each cause with an effect from the box. Write the letter of the effect on the line provided.

Effects:

a. Lewis and Clark were sent to explore the new territory.

b. received help from friendly Native American tribes.

c. created accurate journals that described people, places, and things.

d. Lewis, Clark, and their team had very little to eat.

e. doubling the size of the United States.

f. halting the expedition in order to catch one.

Causes:

1. Lewis and Clark took many breaks to write down everything they saw, which _____.

2. President Jefferson bought the Louisiana territory from France, thus _____.

3. The buffalo moved south for the winter, so _____.

4. Lewis and Clark did not know the land of the Louisiana Purchase, so they _____.

5. Lewis and Clark wanted to examine a prairie dog, which resulted in their _____.

6. President Jefferson wanted to find a water route to the Pacific Ocean, so _____.

© Macmillan/McGraw-Hill

CA **R 2.0** Reading Comprehension (Focus on Informational Materials)

Name _____

As you read *A Historic Journey*, fill in the Cause and Effect Chart.

Cause	➡	Effect
	➡	
	➡	
	➡	
	➡	

How does the information you wrote in this Cause and Effect Chart help
you make inferences and analyze *A Historic Journey*?

© Macmillan/McGraw-Hill

As I read, I will pay attention to punctuation.

	Nature is amazingly complex. Every day many different
8	things happen in nature. Look around and observe. What do
18	you see happening?
21	Living things grow and die as the seasons change. Even the
32	quietest place is not **vacant**. Insects fill the air. Animals search
43	for food and build their homes. Fish and frogs splash in the
55	water. And nature is so **diverse**, too. There are millions of kinds
67	of plants and animals to study.
73	But learning from nature takes time and patience. And that's
83	especially true of animals.
87	You can't just press a button on a hawk and have it tell you
101	how fast it can fly. And chimps don't wear signs telling you
113	how they take care of their young. To learn these things, you
125	have to observe the animals.
130	The people you'll read about here each observed animals in
140	a different way. And each gave the world something through
150	his observations. Some helped us make sense of the natural
160	world. Others helped us see the importance of protecting it. 170

Comprehension Check

1. What does the word *diverse* mean? **Context Clues**

2. What does it take to learn from nature? **Main Idea and Details**

	Words Read	–	Number of Errors	=	Words Correct Score
First Read		–		=	
Second Read		–		=	

 R 1.1 Read aloud narrative and expository text fluently and accurately and with appropriate pacing, intonation, and expression.

A **dictionary** entry tells you what a word means and how to pronounce it. It also tells whether a word is a noun, a verb, or another part of speech. A **thesaurus** entry provides a list of words with similar meanings. It also contains parts of speech for each of the words.

Use the sample dictionary and thesaurus entries in the box to answer the questions below.

Dictionary:
na-ture (ˊnā chər) *n.*: 1. the basic character of a person 2. the physical world, especially living things and objects such as rocks and air

Thesaurus:
Natural: *adj:* normal, typical, regular
Natural: *adj:* inherent, ingrained
Nature: *n:* type, kind

1. How many meanings does the dictionary list for the word *nature*? _____

2. *Ingrained* is another word for _____.

3. Which definition of the word *nature* is the one studied by naturalists? How

   do you know? _____

   _____

4. Write the definition of *nature* that is used in this sentence: *True to her kind*

   nature, the social worker delivered meals to the elderly. _____

   _____

5. What other words might the thesaurus list that mean the same as *nature*?

   _____

W 1.5 Use a thesaurus to identify alternative word choices and meanings.
R 2.0 Reading Comprehension (Focus on Informational Materials)

A Historic Journey • **Grade 5/Unit 2**   **87**

Sequence Writing Frame

A. Summarize _A Historic Journey_. Use the Sequence Writing Frame below.

In 1803, Lewis and Clark _____
_____
_____.

The Louisiana Purchase was important because _____
_____
_____.

In May 1804, _____
_____
_____.

That summer and fall, _____
_____
_____.

The next year, _____
_____
_____.

More than 500 days after they started their journey, _____
_____
_____.

Their trip was important because _____
_____
_____.

B. Rewrite the completed summary on another sheet of paper. Keep it as a model for writing a summary of an article or selection using this text structure.

 R 2.0 Reading Comprehension

Antonyms are words with opposite meanings. A thesaurus
or dictionary is a tool that can help you find antonyms for a
particular word.

**A. Read the paragraph. Write the antonym from the box for each
underlined word.**

| diverse | careful | accurate | land | large | revealed |

   Lewis and Clark made a <u>small</u> _____ contribution

to exploration. Without them the secrets of the enormous <u>ocean</u>

_____ area known as the Louisiana Purchase may have

never been <u>hidden</u> _____. Lewis and Clark were the first

ones to explore the <u>same</u> _____ regions that make up the

United States. They passed through the Great Plains, Badlands, and Rocky

Mountains. They were very <u>careless</u> _____ about taking

<u>incorrect</u> _____ notes about the people, plants, and animals

they came across. With help from friendly Native American tribes, Lewis and

Clark made it all the way to the Pacific Ocean.

**B. Use the antonym word pairs from above to write four sentences.
Underline each antonym.**

1. _____

2. _____

3. _____

4. _____

CA R 1.3 Understand and explain frequently used synonyms, **antonyms,**
and homographs.

A Historic Journey • Grade 5/Unit 2   **89**

Name _____

Using the Word Study Steps

1. LOOK at the word.

2. SAY the word aloud.

3. STUDY the letters in the word.

4. WRITE the word.

5. CHECK the word.
   Did you spell the word right?
   If not, go back to step 1.

X the Words

Put an X on the one word in each line that does not fit the spelling pattern.

1. liberties	possibilities	zeroes	abilities
2. fangs	countries	rodeos	beliefs
3. batches	rattlers	reptiles	fangs
4. lashes	potatoes	identities	notches
5. difficulties	eddies	possibilities	rodeos
6. taxes	abilities	losses	notches
7. reptiles	batches	taxes	potatoes
8. beliefs	rodeos	rattlers	difficulties
9. countries	identities	surroundings	eddies
10. losses	zeroes	lashes	liberties

 LC 1.5 Spell roots, suffixes, prefixes, contractions, and syllable constructions correctly.

Name _____

A. Circle each misspelled word in this report. Write the correctly spelled word on the lines below.

Americans are asked to help their government according to their abilitys. In the United States, as in many other countreys, this means that people must pay taxs. The government uses the money to help citizens, build projects, and defend our libertyes. Sometimes paying the government causes difficultyes, especially if businesses have had losss during the year.

1. _____   3. _____   5. _____

2. _____   4. _____   6. _____

B. Writing Activity

Write a short report about snakes. Use four spelling words in your writing.

_____

_____

_____

_____

_____

_____

_____

_____

_____

_____

_____

LC 1.5 Spell roots, suffixes, prefixes, contractions, and syllable constructions correctly.

Name _____

- Add **-es** to form the plural of singular nouns that end in **s, sh, ch,** or **x**.
- To form the plural of nouns ending in a consonant and **y**, change the **y** to **i** and add **-es**.
- To form the plural of nouns ending in a vowel and **y**, add **-s**.

A. Write the plural of each noun.

1. enemy _____
2. valley _____
3. moss _____
4. bush _____
5. country _____
6. inch _____
7. box _____
8. baby _____
9. patch _____
10. family _____

B. Read each sentence. On the line provided, write the correct plural for each underlined word.

11. Squirrels and rabbits make good <u>lunch</u> _____ for rattlers.

12. Rattlers live in deserts and prairies rather than in <u>city</u> _____.

13. The McCrystals spend many <u>day</u> _____ helping to protect rattlers.

14. Sometimes coyotes and <u>fox</u> _____ eat rattlers.

LC 1.0 Written and Oral English Language Conventions

Name _____

> • A **singular noun** names one person, place, or thing.
> • A **plural noun** names more than one person, place, or thing.
> • Most plural nouns are formed by adding **-s.**
> • Add **-es** to form the plural of singular nouns that end in **s, sh,** **ch,** or **x.**
> • To form the plural of nouns ending in a consonant and **y,** change the **y** to **i** and add **-es.**
> • To form the plural of nouns ending in a vowel and **y,** add **-s.**

Rewrite each sentence. Correct the plural forms.

1. Dad and I walked across wide stretchs of land.

   _____

2. We hiked over tall hills and down into rocky ditchies.

   _____

3. We listened for the soundes that rattlers make.

   _____

4. Any rattlers nearby could feel vibrationes as we walked.

   _____

5. The pites on their faces help them feel our body heat.

   _____

6. We knew that they would rather strike rabbites than people.

   _____

7. People are enemys of rattlers, though, so we were careful.

   _____

8. We saw one long snake with diamond-shaped blotchies on its skin.

   _____

9. More snakes could have been hidden in the grassies.

   _____

10. We heard a hawk's crys as we walked back to our car.

   _____

© Macmillan/McGraw-Hill

LC 1.0 Written and Oral English Language Conventions

Name _____

1. Please read the following sentence:

Sally was scared during the movie.

Now, rewrite this idea in three sentences showing how Sally looked and acted without using the word *scared*.

Example:

Sally covered her eyes and peeked through her fingers while the lion was attacking the gazelle. When the poor gazelle fell to the ground, she gasped. Then she bunched up into a ball in her seat and buried her face in her brother's coat until the scene was over.

_____

_____

_____

_____

Extra Practice: Follow these instructions with the following sentence:

David was angry with his brother after his brother broke his model.

_____

_____

_____

_____

_____

_____

_____

 W 1.0 Writing Strategies

An **inflectional ending** is an ending that is added to a word to show a change in the way the word is used. When you add an inflected ending, follow the spelling rules shown in the examples below to keep the vowel sound of the base word the same. Add **-ing** for present tense and **-ed** for past tense.

Examples:

hope + **-ing** = hoping	Drop the silent **e** so that **hope** keeps a long **o** sound.
hop + **-ing** = hopping	Double the end consonant so that **hop** keeps a short **o** sound.
deny + **-ed** = denied	Change the **y** to **i** so that **deny** keeps a long **e** sound and the long **i** sound of **y**.

Say the words below aloud. Add the correct inflected ending from the box to each base word. Write the new word on the line using the spelling rules. Use the tense in parentheses to help you.

| -ing   -ed |

1. drip (present)   + _____ = _____

2. amuse (present)   + _____ = _____

3. jog (present)   + _____ = _____

4. qualify (past)   + _____ = _____

5. rake (present)   + _____ = _____

6. rely (past)   + _____ = _____

7. forbid (present)   + _____ = _____

8. ease (present)   + _____ = _____

9. apply (past)   + _____ = _____

10. regret (past)   + _____ = _____

© Macmillan/McGraw-Hill

A. Select the correct vocabulary word from the choices in parentheses. Write the word on the line provided.

1. Horses were important to the cowboy's job. They enabled the cowboy to travel easily over the (vastness, horizon) of the countryside.

   _____

2. The cowboys had great (hunger, enthusiasm) for their job and eagerly helped the rancher herd the cattle. _____

3. Sometimes it seemed as though the horses could ride all the way to the (horizon, vastness), where the land met the sky. _____

4. The (vastness, presence) of the horses helped keep the cattle under control. _____

5. Both cows and horses had to be careful not to slip into a (horizon, ravine). Such a steep, narrow canyon was a danger. _____

6. Horses (suspended, swerved) around the cows to keep the herd moving in the right direction. _____

7. The rattlesnake's rattle made a (distinct, suspended) sound that every cowboy knew. _____

8. The horses slept with the cowboys' spurs (swerved, suspended) from the top of their saddles. _____

B. Write new sentences for two of the vocabulary words used above. Then underline the vocabulary word.

9. _____

   _____

10. _____

    _____

 CA R 1.0 Word Analysis, Fluency, and Systematic Vocabulary Development

© Macmillan/McGraw-Hill

Name _____

As you read *Black Cowboy, Wild Horses*, fill in the Inferences Chart.

Text Clues	What You Know	Inferences

How does the information you wrote in the Inferences Chart help you monitor comprehension of *Black Cowboy, Wild Horses*?

 R 2.4 Draw inferences, conclusions, or generalizations about text and support them with textual evidence and prior knowledge.

© Macmillan/McGraw-Hill

Name _____ Chav _____

As I read, I will pay attention to pacing.

	Alice was born in 1902 on a ranch near Red Lodge,
11	Montana. Because they traveled on horses, the Greenough
19	family kept dozens of them to ride. Alice also fed cattle,
30	roped them, and rounded them up. She developed the riding
40	and roping skills that would later bring her fame.
49	Alice had seven brothers and sisters, five of whom wound
59	up working in rodeos. They became known as the "Riding
69	Greenoughs." Alice later said, "We learned to ride before we
79	could walk."
81	Ranch life was busy. The family planted, grew, and
90	harvested crops. Cattle had to be rounded up and fed.
100	Someone had to tame the horses and teach them to carry a
112	rider) or pull a wagon. In addition, the fences needed fixing,
123	and the buildings and machines needed repairs. 130

Comprehension Check

1. What were some of the chores on the Greenoughs' ranch? **Main Idea and Details**

2. Why do you think five of the Greenoughs ended up working in rodeos? **Plot Development**

	Words Read	–	Number of Errors	=	Words Correct Score
First Read		–		=	
Second Read		–		=	

R 1.1 Read aloud narrative and expository text fluently and accurately and with appropriate pacing, intonation, and expression.

Black Cowboy, Wild Horses
Grade 5/Unit 2

© Macmillan/McGraw-Hill

Name _____

When you read poetry, pay attention to features often used with poetic language. For example, poems often include **repetition**, which occurs when a line or a sequence of lines appears more than once. **Assonance** is the repetition of the same or similar vowel sounds in a series of words, usually words with different consonant sounds. Repetition and assonance give poems a musical quality and rhythm.

Read the poem. Then answer the questions.

1 There once was a filly named Blaze,
2 Who wouldn't come out of the rain.
3 First that filly got soaked.
4 Then she grew hoarse and croaked,
5 Which put out that filly named Blaze.

1. In which lines do you see repetition? _____

_____

2. What is the example of assonance in the repeated words? _____

_____

3. What other examples of assonance do you see in line 1? _____

_____

4. What is the example of assonance in line 2? _____

_____

5. Is there an example of assonance in line 3? _____

_____

6. Is there an example of assonance in line 4? _____

_____

© Macmillan/McGraw-Hill

 CA R 2.0 Reading Comprehension

An **analogy** is a statement that compares two pairs of words. The relationship between the two words in the first pair is the same as the relationship between the two words in the second pair. **Antonyms**, two words with opposite meanings, can be used in analogies.

criticize	cry	energetic	absence	soft

Complete each analogy by providing an appropriate antonym from the box. Then write a sentence using antonyms from the analogy.

1. feebly is to strongly as tired is to _____

_____

_____

2. presence is to _____ as arrive is to depart

_____

_____

3. light is to heavy as _____ is to hard

_____

_____

4. awake is to asleep as praise is to _____

_____

_____

5. laugh is to _____ as smile is to frown

_____

_____

© Macmillan/McGraw-Hill

R 1.3 Understand and explain frequently used synonyms, antonyms, and homographs.

Black Cowboy, Wild Horses
Grade 5/Unit 2

101

Name _____

Using the Word Study Steps

1. LOOK at the word.
2. SAY the word aloud.
3. STUDY the letters in the word.

4. WRITE the word.
5. CHECK the word.
   Did you spell the word right?
   If not, go back to step 1.

A. Find and Circle

Find and circle each of the spelling words in this puzzle. Words may read forward, backward, upward, downward, or diagonally.

```
G  Q  A  D  S  L  F  M  R  G  D  A  R  Z  T  J  Y  C
N  U  P  E  K  F  F  A  N  E  K  B  M  G  Q  F  O  O
I  A  P  I  Y  B  S  I  T  D  E  V  R  E  S  E  D  M
N  L  L  V  X  I  W  A  D  E  T  T  E  R  G  E  R  P
E  I  I  N  V  E  N  G  N  I  K  A  R  B  G  K  D  L
T  F  E  E  N  I  D  R  I  P  P  I  N  G  N  G  E  I
A  I  D  E  C  G  N  I  S  U  M  A  S  E  A  N  M  C
E  E  R  S  O  I  N  J  U  R  E  D  N  A  R  I  M  A
R  D  A  D  E  I  L  E  R  C  O  K  G  S  L  G  I  T
H  F  F  O  R  B  I  D  D  I  N  G  S  I  E  G  K  E
T  P  R  G  D  D  E  R  R  E  F  E  R  N  D  O  S  D
A  C  C  E  P  T  E  D  R  X  Y  Q  N  G  S  J  Q  R
```

B. List the words below as you find them in the puzzle.

1. _____   6. _____   11. _____   16. _____

2. _____   7. _____   12. _____   17. _____

3. _____   8. _____   13. _____   18. _____

4. _____   9. _____   14. _____   19. _____

5. _____   10. _____   15. _____   20. _____

LC 1.5 Spell roots, suffixes, prefixes, contractions, and syllable constructions correctly.

A. Circle the misspelled words in the passage. Write the words correctly on the lines below.

Maya Lin stood there, getting ready to give her speech. She skimd her notes, making sure that nothing was missing. She had applide for the job three weeks ago, knowing that she was qualifide. Now that she worked at the museum, she regrettid not knowing about the job sooner. She began her speech with an amyusing story to relieve some of the pressure. Within minutes, the audience was fassinated.

1. _____   3. _____   5. _____

2. _____   4. _____   6. _____

Writing Activity

B. Write a paragraph about something you can do to honor those who have lost their lives in service to their country. Use four words from your spelling list.

_____

_____

_____

_____

_____

_____

_____

_____

_____

_____

_____

_____

LC 1.5 Spell roots, suffixes, prefixes, contractions, and syllable constructions correctly.

Black Cowboy, Wild Horses
Grade 5/Unit 2   103

Name _____

- To form the plural of nouns that end with a vowel and **o**, add **-s**.
- To form the plural of nouns that end with a consonant and **o**, add **-s** or **-es**.
- Some nouns have special forms.
- A few nouns have the same singular and plural forms.

A. Write the plural of each noun.

1. radio _____

2. piano _____

3. stereo _____

4. banjo _____

5. kangaroo _____

B. Read each sentence. On the line provided, write the correct form of any incorrect plural nouns.

6. Learning about the past is like hearing echos from history.

   _____

7. Monuments and museums help us remember American heros.

   _____

8. Architect Maya Lin designed a civil rights monument that is nine foots

   high. _____

9. Memorials have been built to honor both men and womans.

   _____

10. We can learn about brave people by reading books or watching

    videoes. _____

LC 1.0 Written and Oral English Language Conventions

© Macmillan/McGraw-Hill

- To form the plural of most nouns ending in **f** or **fe**, add **-s.**
- For other nouns, change the **f** to **v** and add **-es**.
- To form the plural of nouns that end with a vowel and **o**, add **-s**.
- To form the plural of nouns that end with a consonant and **o**, add **-s** or **-es**.
- Some nouns have special forms.
- A few nouns have the same singular and plural forms.

Read the following paragraph. Then rewrite the paragraph, changing any incorrect plural nouns.

Adults and childs enjoy visiting the National Air and Space Museum. This museum has the largest collection of aircraftes in the world. It is hard to believe that persons flew in some of those early planes. They were brave to risk their lifes.

_____

_____

_____

_____

_____

_____

_____

_____

_____

_____

Name _____

Writing Rubric

4 Excellent	3 Good	2 Fair	1 Unsatisfactory
Ideas and Content/ Genre	Ideas and Content/ Genre	Ideas and Content/ Genre	Ideas and Content/ Genre
Organization and Focus	Organization and Focus	Organization and Focus	Organization and Focus
Sentence Structure/ Fluency	Sentence Structure/ Fluency	Sentence Structure/ Fluency	Sentence Structure/ Fluency
Conventions	Conventions	Conventions	Conventions
Word Choice	Word Choice	Word Choice	Word Choice
Voice	Voice	Voice	Voice
Presentation	Presentation	Presentation	Presentation

Name _____

> A **contraction** is a shortened form of two words. An apostrophe takes the place of the missing letters.
> she is = she's   he will = he'll

A. Write the words each contraction stands for.

1. shouldn't _____

2. don't _____

3. you're _____

4. he's _____

5. won't _____

B. Write the contraction that takes the place of the underlined words.

1. Sue <u>could not</u> decide which book to check out from the library.

_____

2. <u>She had</u> read a mystery last week. _____

3. She <u>did not</u> want to read a nonfiction book. _____

4. "I think <u>I will</u> read a tall tale about Sluefoot Sue," she decided.

_____

5. "<u>It will</u> be fun to read about a character who shares my name."

_____

Name _____

A. Choose a word from the box to complete each sentence.

impress	wring	posed	original
commenced	advertisement	elected	sauntered

1. I just saw an _____ for a new book about Davy Crockett.

2. Davy Crockett packed his bag and _____ his trip.

3. Davy Crockett could easily _____ people because he could do so many things.

4. Davy Crockett had to _____ a dead limb off a big oak tree.

5. Davy Crockett _____ for a picture with the President.

6. He was _____ to Congress when he received more votes than anyone else.

7. I _____ back to the library, thinking about Davy Crockett as I strolled along.

8. The _____ tall tale about Davy Crockett was told in the 1800s.

B. Write new sentences for two of the vocabulary words used above. Then underline the vocabulary word.

9. _____

_____

10. _____

_____

 R 1.0 Word Analysis, Fluency, and Systematic Vocabulary Development

The **plot** is the series of events in a story that take the characters through an experience or change. In some stories, the plot includes a problem that a character must solve. The **setting** is where and when the story takes place.

Read the tall tale below. Identify the setting and the events in the plot.

When a speeding comet threatened to crash into Earth, everyone turned to Davy Crockett for help. Davy Crockett was the biggest, strongest, most courageous man alive. If anyone could save Earth, Davy Crockett could!

Everyone gathered around Davy as he prepared to climb the tallest mountain in Texas. "I'll hop right up to the top of this mountain," he exclaimed, "and grab that comet by the tail. I'll toss it away quicker than you can say 'howdy-do.'"

The people held their breath as Davy took long strides up the mountain. His legs were a blur because they moved so quickly. The crowd gasped when Davy disappeared into the clouds. Would Davy stop the comet?

Just then, the crowd jumped back with a loud roar. Davy had grabbed the comet's tail. He twirled the comet around like a lasso and then sent it flying into outer space.

Davy hadn't even begun to sweat! Davy Crockett proved once again that there was nothing he couldn't do.

Summary: _____

_____

_____

_____

_____

_____

_____

CA **R 2.2** Analyze text that is organized in sequential or chronological order.

Davy Crockett Saves the World
Grade 5/Unit 2   109

Name _____

As you read *Davy Crockett Saves the World*, fill in the
Plot and Setting Chart.

Plot	Setting

How does the information you wrote in this Plot and Setting Chart help you
analyze the story structure of *Davy Crockett Saves the World*?

R 2.2 Analyze text that is organized in sequential or chronological
order.

Name _____ Chew _____

As I read, I will pay attention to my expression.

	Back then it wasn't easy to feed a large family. Luckily
11	Johnny possessed a green thumb. From the time that he was
22	two years old, it seemed as if Johnny could just look at
34	a seed and a plant commenced to grow. So Johnny and his
46	green thumb fed his large family.
52	There was plenty of food, but dinnertime was extremely
61	noisy in Johnny's house. Why, it was as if a volcano was
73	exploding at dinnertime! As soon as the food hit the table,
84	the children shouted and complained.
89	"Tommy's apple pie is bigger than mine!"
96	"Why are we having apple juice again?"
103	All that noise gave Johnny a headache, so he would take
114	his dinner outside and escape to his favorite spot, the apple
125	orchard. There, Johnny felt at home. 131

Comprehension Check

1. What kind of person was Johnny? **Character**

Tommy

2. How did Johnny's family benefit from his green thumb? **Plot Development**

	Words Read	−	Number of Errors	=	Words Correct Score
First Read	125	−	1	=	124
Second Read	130	−	1	=	130

R 1.1 Read aloud narrative and expository text fluently and accurately and with appropriate pacing, intonation, and expression.

Davy Crockett Saves the World
Grade 5/Unit 2   **111**

Name _____

A **toolbar** is a strip of symbols that allows you to visit different features on a Web site. A **link** is an electronic connection on a Web site that provides direct access to other information.

Use the Web site page to answer the questions.

www.example.com

Social Studies

| Home | Browse | Search | Tall Tales |

THE TALES ARE GETTING TALLER

by Kyle Seulen

Have you ever visited or seen pictures of Puget Sound in Washington State or the Black Hills of South Dakota? If so, you have seen some of Paul Bunyan's greatest work. One time, when Paul was headed out West, he dragged his giant pickax behind him, and the ditch he made with it was the Grand Canyon. This statement may be **exaggerating** the facts just a little. Paul Bunyan really did not make these beautiful places, but the stories we like to tell about him make him one of the heroes of American tall tales.

Tall tale heroes and the regions where they were born

What is a tall tale? Four features make a story a tall tale. First, the hero must seem larger than life and have **superhuman** skills. Second, the hero usually has a certain job that he does better than anyone else. The hero might be a lumberjack or a cowhand, for example. Third, the hero must solve a problem in a way that surprises the reader or makes the audience laugh. Fourth, the details of the tale are exaggerated

to be made greater than they really are. Often, the hero is bursting with courage and ready to conquer any difficulty. As a rule, the heroes would be a little rough on the outside. Still, they had tender hearts and souls and possessed the most admirable qualities. They were helpful, always available to solve problems and determined to create a better world for their neighbors and friends.

Links related to this topic

Related Articles

▶ Paul Bunyan
▶ John Henry
▶ Davy Crockett
▶ Pecos Bill

1. Why is the toolbar important? _Pecos bill_

_____

2. What do links do? _The link related to this topic._

_____

_____

3. On this Web site, how else would you get information on tall tales?

google

_____

R 2.1 Understand how text features (e.g., format, graphics, sequence, diagrams, illustrations, charts, maps) make information accessible and usable.

Sometimes two smaller words are put together to form a **compound word**. Recognizing the smaller words can help you figure out the compound word's meaning. For example, **newspaper** is a compound word made from the words **news** and **paper**. The word **newspaper** means "paper on which news is published."

Underline the compound word in each sentence. Then use the meaning of smaller words to help you write the compound word's meaning.

1. The storyteller told an exciting tale about Davy Crockett. _That_
   he save the world

2. One story is about how Pecos Bill tames a whirlwind. _____

3. I wrote a story about Sluefoot Sue in my notebook. _____

4. The townspeople decided to ask Davy Crockett for help. _Save the_
   world

5. We could see for miles from the top of the skyscraper. _____

6. For dinner, Davy Crockett ate homegrown tomatoes in his salad. _____

7. Today we will cut the grass with our electric lawnmower. _____

8. I bought some groceries and a magazine from the shopkeeper. _____

Using the Word Study Steps

1. LOOK at the word.
2. SAY the word aloud.
3. STUDY the letters in the word.
4. WRITE the word.
5. CHECK the word.
   Did you spell the word right?
   If not, go back to step 1.

A. Word Combining

Combine the two short words to write a spelling word.

1. you + have = _you've_
2. would + not = _wouldn't_
3. do + not = _don't_
4. we + will = _we'll_
5. they + are = _they're_
6. could + not = _couldn't_
7. we + are = _we're_
8. I + have = _I've_
9. there + is = _there's_
10. does + not = _doesn't_

B. Fill in the missing letters to write a spelling word. You will use one of the blanks for the apostrophe.

11. y _o_ u _a_ r _e_
12. d _i_ d n _o_ t
13. h _____ _____ d
14. i _____ _____ _____ t
15. w _____ _____ t _____ s

LC 1.5 Spell roots, suffixes, prefixes, contractions, and syllable
constructions correctly.

© Macmillan/McGraw-Hill

Name _____

A. Circle the misspelled words in the passage. Write the words correctly on the lines below.

W'ere in a heap of trouble! Halley's Comet is speeding toward Earth. It is getting bigger every day. If someone dos'nt do something soon, it will crash into our planet.

The President says we shoudn't worry. Theres help on the way. Davy Crockett will pull the tail off the comet. There isnt anything he can't do. Best of all, thats not even something he expects to be paid for. He says he enjoys the challenge.

1. ___doesn't___   3. ___We're___   5. ___expect___

2. _____   4. _____   6. _____

Writing Activity

B. Imagine that you are larger than life, like a tall-tale hero. What kind of adventure might you have? Write a tall tale about yourself, using at least four spelling words.

_____

_____

_____

_____

_____

_____

_____

_____

LC 1.5 Spell roots, suffixes, prefixes, contractions, and syllable constructions correctly.

Davy Crockett Saves the World
Grade 5/Unit 2

115

- A plural **possessive noun** is a plural noun that shows ownership.
- To form the possessive of a plural noun that ends in **-s**, add an apostrophe.
- To form the possessive of a plural noun that does not end in **-s**, add an apostrophe and **-s**.

Read each sentence. Write the correct possessive noun on the line.

1. José Manuel found the three girls note in the basket. _____

2. All the houses balconies had beautiful railings. _____

3. Both doors hinges squeaked. _____

4. Grandmas frown made them feel a little frightened. _____

5. Amalia called her sisters names to get their attention. _____

6. The girls smelled the corn fritters aroma, so they stayed longer.

   _____

7. When the girls got home, Mamis face showed that she was upset.

   _____

8. The sisters hadn't asked their mothers permission to invite José Manuel.

   _____

9. The childrens trip to the beach was special because José Manuel

   joined them. _____

10. Evelyns wish for José Manuel will come true. _____

 LC 1.0 Written and Oral English Language Conventions

Name _____ chau _____

As I read, I will pay attention to pronunciation.

	The fight for women's rights started with the fight to end
11	slavery. Beginning in the 1820s, many women became active
19	in the struggle for the abolition (ab-uh-LISH-uhn), or end,
27	of slavery.
29	One woman who worked hard to fight slavery was
38	Lucretia Mott. In 1833, she started a women's antislavery
46	society in Philadelphia. She went to London to attend the
56	first World's Anti-Slavery Convention. Women had to sit
64	behind a curtain. They couldn't be seen or heard. Lucretia
74	Mott was furious.
77	Also attending the London convention was Elizabeth
84	Cady Stanton. She, too, was angry at the limited role that
95	women were allowed. She and Mott became friends. Mott
104	was some 20 years older, but they shared many of the
114	same views.
116	The two friends began to talk with other women who
126	were working to free the slaves. They talked about how hard
137	women's lives were. They talked about the need to make
147	changes. They talked about how they might work together to
157	fight for their own rights. 162

Comprehension Check

1. What does the word *abolition* mean? **Context Clues**

2. How did Lucretia Mott fight to end slavery? **Main Idea and Details**

	Words Read	–	Number of Errors	=	Words Correct Score
First Read	95	–	4	=	91
Second Read	162	–	2	=	160

R 1.1 Read aloud narrative and expository text fluently and accurately
and with appropriate pacing, intonation, and expression.

A **time line** is a diagram of several events arranged in the order in which they took place. A time line helps to arrange information in an easy, visual way.

Important Events in the Women's Suffrage Movement

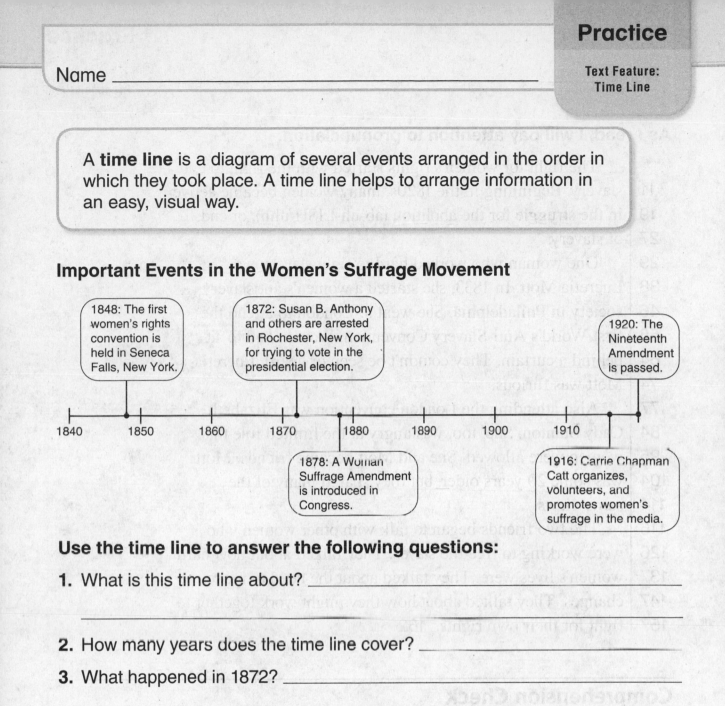

1848: The first women's rights convention is held in Seneca Falls, New York.

1872: Susan B. Anthony and others are arrested in Rochester, New York, for trying to vote in the presidential election.

1920: The Nineteenth Amendment is passed.

1840 1850 1860 1870 1880 1890 1900 1910

1878: A Woman Suffrage Amendment is introduced in Congress.

1916: Carrie Chapman Catt organizes, volunteers, and promotes women's suffrage in the media.

Use the time line to answer the following questions:

1. What is this time line about? _____

_____

2. How many years does the time line cover? _____

3. What happened in 1872? _____

_____

4. Where was the first women's rights conference in the United States held?

_____

5. Who traveled across America to organize volunteers?

_____

6. Which happened first: Seneca Falls Convention or the Nineteenth

Amendment is ratified? _____

R 2.1 Understand how text features (e.g., format, graphics, sequence, diagrams, illustrations, charts, maps) make information accessible and usable.

Use a dictionary when you want to check **word origins**. The
definition may include information about the word's beginnings
or how it has changed over time. It also may tell which language
a word comes from or how or when a word became part of the
English language.

**Find each of these words in the dictionary. Next to each word, tell
the language from which the word comes.**

1. taco _____

2. junk _____

3. car _____

4. reason _____

5. magenta _____

6. tortilla _____

7. city _____

8. dollar _____

9. guitar _____

10. cereal _____

11. music _____

12. radius _____

CA **R 1.2** Use word origins to determine the meaning of unknown words.

Name _____

Using the Word Study Steps

1. LOOK at the word.

2. SAY the word aloud.

3. STUDY the letters in the word.

4. WRITE the word.

5. CHECK the word.
   Did you spell the word right?
   If not, go back to step 1.

A. Fill in the missing letters of each word to form a spelling word.

1. ke _____ _____ el

2. cha _____ _____ ion

3. vu _____ _____ ure

4. ho _____ _____ ow

5. a _____ _____ ent

6. mu _____ _____ ang

7. su _____ _____ it

8. fla _____ _____ er

9. e _____ _____ iro

10. go _____ les

11. pi _____ _____ ent

12. fra _____ _____ ent

13. va _____ _____ ey

14. cu _____ _____ ure

15. ga _____ _____ op

16. su _____ _____ on

17. bli _____ _____ ard

18. fi _____ _____ een

19. jo _____ _____ or

20. de _____ ist

B. Use the spelling words above to write a poem of at least 4 lines.

21. _____

22. _____

23. _____

24. _____

CA **LC 1.5** Spell roots, suffixes, prefixes, contractions, and syllable constructions correctly.

Name _____

A. Circle each incorrectly spelled word in this diary entry. Write the words correctly on the lines below.

I like to read about the old West. There are great stories about the cullture of the ranchers and cowboys. I like to imagine what it would be like to galop away on a mustang. Cowboys and cowgirls faced danger often. They could be lost in a valey or caught in a blizzerd. Even in a safe place, they could be hurt by a fragment of stone thrown from a horse's hoof. The wide and empty range must have felt like the cowboy's emmpire.

1. _____   3. _____   5. _____

2. _____   4. _____   6. _____

Writing Activity

B. Write a letter to Bob or another cowboy or cowgirl. Use four words from the spelling list.

_____

_____

_____

_____

_____

_____

_____

_____

_____

_____

_____

CA **LC 1.5** Spell roots, suffixes, prefixes, contractions, and syllable constructions correctly.

- A **possessive noun** shows who or what owns or has something.
- Add an apostrophe and **-s** to a singular noun to make it possessive.
- Add an apostrophe to make most plural nouns possessive.

Read these paragraphs and study the noun choices in parentheses. In each case, draw a line under the correct noun form.

Bob knew that he had to have the (earth's/earths) smell on him before the (horses/horses') would accept him. He couldn't even build a fire because the animals could smell the smoke on his clothes from (miles'/miles) away.

At the (dawn's/dawns) early light, Bob saddled up to search for the herd. When a storm struck, Warrior reared and pawed at the air with his (hooves'/hooves). Lightning brightened the sky, and Bob saw the (mustangs'/mustangs) for the first time.

The storm had washed away the (herds, herd's) tracks, but Bob knew where to look for them. He rode to the big river and waited. Finally, the herd arrived. The lead stallion sniffed the air and looked in (Bobs, Bob's) direction. Bob remained perfectly still. When the (horses/horse's) began to graze, he knew he had been accepted. If the stallion trusted him, Bob would have the (mares'/mares) trust, too.

 LC 1.0 Written and Oral English Language Conventions

- A **plural noun** names more than one person, place, or thing.
- Add **-s** or **-es** to most nouns to form the plural. Do not use an apostrophe.
- A **possessive noun** shows who or what owns or has something.
- Add an apostrophe and **-s** to a singular noun to make it possessive.
- Add an apostrophe to make most plural nouns possessive.

Read the following paragraph. Then rewrite the paragraph, correcting mistakes in the formation of singular and plural possessive nouns and plural nouns.

Cowboy's spent a lot of time on horseback. Horses' allowed them to cover great distances when herding ranchers cattle. The cowboys rode horses called mustangs. Mustangs were fast and strong, so they made good cow ponie's. The mustang's had to be tamed before anyone could ride them.

_____

_____

_____

_____

_____

_____

_____

_____

1. Read the following sentence:

Maria took Sara's picture.

2. Now rewrite this sentence to SHOW the emotions listed below:

SHY: Sara covered her face with her magazine when Maria tried to take her picture.

_____

_____

HAPPY: When Maria took her picture, Sara's smile was so big, it looked as if her cheeks might burst.

_____

_____

CONFUSED: When she tried to take Sara's picture, Maria looked into the wrong side of the camera and the flash went off in her eyes.

_____

_____

Extra Practice: Do the same exercise using the following telling sentence:

Carrie walked into a room full of people.

 W 1.0 Writing Strategies

Name _____

The point where two syllables meet determines whether the vowel sound in the first syllable is long or short. A syllable that ends in a vowel (as in *hu-man*) is an **open syllable**. It has a **V/CV pattern,** and the vowel sound is long. A syllable that ends in a consonant (as in *wag-on*) is a closed syllable. It has a **VC/V pattern,** and the vowel sound is short.

Say the words below and break them into syllables. Then write the words in syllables on the lines provided. Write *long* if the word has a V/CV pattern. Write *short* if the word has a VC/V pattern.

1. humor _____   _____

2. pilot _____   _____

3. lemon _____   _____

4. punish _____   _____

5. lazy _____   _____

6. legal _____   _____

7. comet _____   _____

8. profile _____   _____

9. frozen _____   _____

10. proper _____   _____

11. waken _____   _____

12. tuna _____   _____

© Macmillan/McGraw-Hill

Name _____

| appreciation | wares | treasurer | merchandise |
| educate | burdens | instruct | unfortunate |

Replace the underlined word or words in each sentence with a word from the box.

1. The story of the fisher can <u>teach</u> readers about how people's greed can often get them in trouble. _educate_

2. The Market Club hired a <u>person who manages money</u> to help count all the money made at the market. _treasurer_

3. At the market, the basketmaker set out her <u>collection of wares</u> for all to see. _wares_

4. The fisher tricked others into leaving part of their <u>heavy loads</u> with him. _appreciation_

5. He tried to <u>direct</u> people to cross the river at the log. _merchandise_

6. Each person carefully carried his or her <u>products</u> across the log in order to reach the market. _instruct_

7. He hoped that people would express their <u>gratitude</u> by paying him well. _burdens_

8. The fisher's plan did not work, and he felt very <u>unlucky</u>. _unfortunate_

 CA R 1.0 Word Analysis, Fluency, and Systematic Vocabulary Development

© Macmillan/McGraw-Hill

Name _____ Chau V _____

An **author's purpose** is his or her reason for writing the story. The purpose may be to inform, to entertain, to persuade, or to explain.

Read the summary of *The Catch of the Day*. Then answer the questions about the author's purpose.

A griot introduced himself as a keeper of history, a teacher, and a storyteller, and told a group of children a story of a fisher who decided to trick many people who were trying to get to the market. The fisher shook a log to convince each person it was unsafe to cross with so much merchandise. Finally, the ones who were tricked discovered what the fisher was up to and decided to trick him. As the fisher crossed the bridge, they shook the log so hard that he fell into the water. On the riverbank, the people the fisher tricked laughed and laughed. And later that day they ate a fine fish dinner!

1. When the griot explains who he is, is the author's main purpose to explain, to entertain, to persuade, or to inform? Explain.

   _____

   _____

2. When the author describes how the fisher was tricked, is her main purpose to entertain, to explain, to persuade, or to inform? Explain.

   _____

   _____

3. In what ways might the author's purpose be to persuade people?

   _____

   _____

4. What do you think is the author's purpose for writing *The Catch of the Day*?

   _____

   _____

Name _____

As you read *The Catch of the Day*, fill in the Author's Purpose Chart.

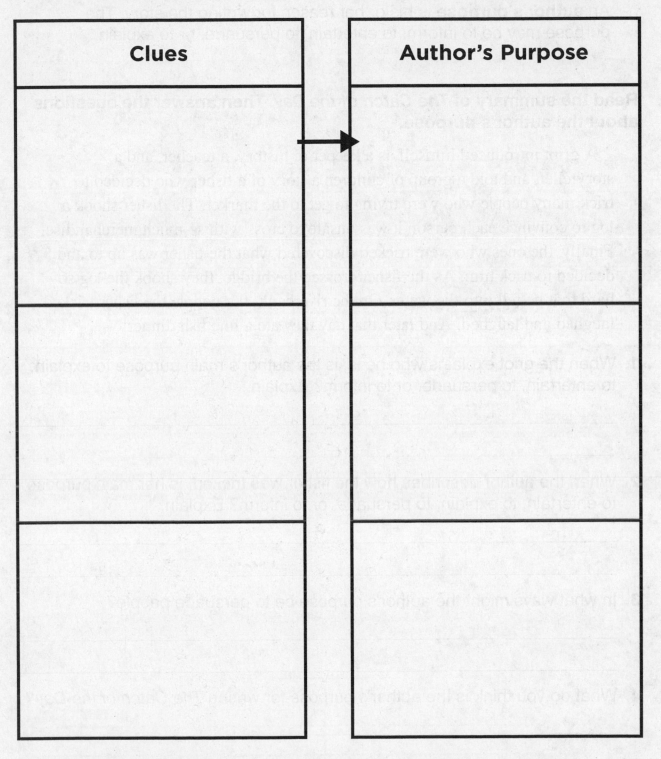

Clues	Author's Purpose

How does the information you wrote in the Author's Purpose Chart help
you evaluate *The Catch of the Day*?

CA **R 2.0** Reading Comprehension (Focus on Informational Materials)

As I read, I will pay attention to pacing.

11	**NARRATOR 1:** Well, at least it isn't a raging river that Brer Rabbit has to cross, just a creek. Though it is higher than
23	usual, and the rain is still coming down hard.
32	**BRER RABBIT:** (*to the audience*) Well, that wasn't too bad.
42	If getting my feet a little wet is the most **unfortunate** thing
54	that happens tonight, I'll be just fine. (*He shakes off the*
65	*wetness and looks around. Then, putting his hand to his ear,*
76	*he listens for a moment.*) Music! I do believe I hear a party
89	shaping up! (*He rubs his hands together eagerly.*) And that
99	means dancing, and dancing means food to feed the dancers,
109	and that means a fine time is had by all. (*He heads offstage*
122	*with a hop, skip, and a jump.*)
129	**NARRATOR 2:** And indeed, a fine time is had by all,
139	especially Brer Rabbit, who doesn't give another thought to
148	the weather. He tries every dance and every dish and finds
159	them all to his total satisfaction. **165**

Comprehension Check

1. What does Brer Rabbit enjoy about parties? **Main Idea and Details**

2. How does Brer Rabbit feel about the weather? **Plot Development**

	Words Read	–	Number of Errors	=	Words Correct Score
First Read		–		=	
Second Read		–		=	

R 1.1 Read aloud narrative and expository text fluently and accurately and with appropriate **pacing**, intonation, and expression.

The Catch of the Day
Grade 5/Unit 3   135

Name _____

> **Similes** and **metaphors** are figures of speech that compare or
> associate two things. They use language to create striking or
> unexpected images for the reader. **Similes** use *like* or *as* in the
> comparison. **Metaphors** do not use *like* or *as*.

Read the tale to answer the following questions.

One day Fox was strolling through the woods when Tiger crept up behind
him as silently as a whisper. Then he pounced. Fox said, "Why are you trying
to harm me? I am King of the Jungle."

Tiger was surprised. "You are as crazy as a monkey," he said. "You aren't
King."

"Of course I am," Fox answered. "The other animals scatter like flies
when they see me. Follow me." Fox went into the forest with Tiger behind
him. When the deer saw Tiger behind Fox, they ran like the wind at the sight
of them.

Then they came across monkeys. At the sight of Tiger behind Fox, the
monkeys were statues, frozen in their trees. Then they fled.

Tiger said, "I'm as shocked as a child at a surprise party, but you are right.
I'm sorry for bothering you, King." Tiger bowed to Fox, and Fox continued
his walk.

1. What is one simile you can find in the tale? _____

_____

_____

2. How are the two things in the simile you chose related?

_____

3. What is the metaphor in the tale? _____

4. How is it different from simile? _____

CA R 3.5 Describe the function and effect of common literary devices
(e.g., imagery, metaphor, symbolism).

Name _____

An **analogy** shows the **relationship** between two pairs of words. The relationship between the two words in the first pair is the same as the relationship between the two words in the second pair.

drink	story	crops	baskets	fingers
fox	merchandise	hopping	leather	fish
song	eagle	painter	needle	mailbox

Choose a word from the box to complete each analogy.

1. Banker is to money as farmer is to _____drink_____.
2. Library is to books as store is to _____story_____.
3. Bird is to flying as rabbit is to _____fox_____.
4. Baker is to bread as basketmaker is to _____baskets_____.
5. Nibble is to eat as sip is to _____needle_____.
6. Yam is to vegetable as trout is to _____fish_____.
7. Clap is to hands as snap is to _____crops_____.
8. Vain is to crow as sneaky is to _____fingers_____.
9. Shirt is to cloth as shoes are to _____merchandise_____.
10. Poet is to poem as author is to _____song_____.
11. Griot is to story as singer is to _____hopping_____.
12. Dog is to wolf as parrot is to _____eagle_____.
13. Microscope is to scientist as paintbrush is to _____painter_____.
14. E-mail is to computer as letter is to _____mailbox_____.

© Macmillan/McGraw-Hill

Name _____

Using the Word Study Steps

1. LOOK at the word.

2. SAY the word aloud.

3. STUDY the letters in the word.

4. WRITE the word.

5. CHECK the word.
   Did you spell the word right?
   If not, go back to step 1.

Find and Circle

A. Where are the spelling words?

l i n e n c j g l e g a l w p x s t u d e n t h u m o r t u h o
b r d c a v e r n e m i n u s b z t p r o f i l e e t l e q u a l
p u n i s h t o m t y r a n t e y y s m o k y u a t r e c e n t
g i s v a c a n t h p a n i c m u c l o c a l b z t s h i v e r
c o m e t h w v l o s e r f t r d e c e n t l o k c l o s e t e r

B. Write the words below as you find them in the puzzle.

1. humor
2. legal
3. comet
4. local
5. equal
6. close
7. recent
8.
9.
10.
11.
12.
13.
14.
15.
16.
17.
18.
19.
20.

 LC 1.5 Spell roots, suffixes, prefixes, contractions, and syllable constructions correctly.

Name _____

A. Circle the misspelled words in this paragraph. Write the words correctly on the lines below.

Colin felt that General Gage was a desent man, and not a tierant like King George. General Gage understood that a studdent like Colin enjoyed sledding on a locall hill during recess. General Gage didn't even punnish Colin for being so bold in asking him to remove the tents from the hill. Even though the cold wind made Colin shivver, he was happy that General Gage had made it possible to go sledding.

1. _____   3. _____   5. _____

2. _____   4. _____   6. _____

B. Writing Activity

Think about something that you like to do. Has there ever been a time when you couldn't do it and you had to ask someone's permission to help you? Write about what happened, or what you think might happen, in this situation. Use four spelling words.

_____

_____

_____

_____

_____

_____

_____

_____

_____

_____

LC 1.5 Spell roots, suffixes, prefixes, contractions, and syllable constructions correctly.

The Catch of the Day
Grade 5/Unit 3   **139**

© Macmillan/McGraw-Hill

Name _____

- An **action verb** is a word that tells what happens or happened.
- A verb must agree with its subject. A singular subject takes a singular verb. A plural subject takes a plural verb.
- Add *-s* to most verbs in the present tense if the subject is singular.
- If the subject is plural, the verb must be plural. Do not add *-s* to the verb if the subject is a plural noun.

Circle each action verb in these sentences. If the verb does not agree with the subject, write the correct verb on the line following the sentence. All sentences should be in the present tense.

1. Rebels fights for independence. _____

2. The British troops destroys the children's snow forts. _____

3. Henry's father make a sled for Henry. _____

4. The soldiers break the ice in the pond. _____

5. Henry's brothers walks to school with Henry. _____

6. General Gage help the children. _____

7. King George punishes the colonists. _____

8. The children pulls their sleds through the snow. _____

 LC 1.0 Written and Oral English Language Conventions

- Be sure that the verb agrees with the subject.
- Be sure that each sentence begins with a capital letter and ends with the correct punctuation mark.
- Use commas to separate three or more words or phrases in a series.

In the passage below, circle verbs that don't agree with their subjects. Also, circle mistakes in spelling, capitalization, and punctuation. Then rewrite the passage correctly, adding commas where needed.

The sun rest over the still water. Henry, joshua and Nathan sit at the edge of the pier and gaze out at the empty sea. The only movement in the harbur is at the far end, where British soldiers are getting a ship ready to sail.

Joshua, the yungest man in the group, reach into his pockets. "I have no money," he announces to Henry and nathan.

Nathan looks at Joshua and says "None of us has money,"

Henry run his fingers through his gray hair and says, "we need to get back to work." He pauses and looks out at the sea? "We need our harbor back."

_____

_____

_____

_____

_____

_____

_____

_____

_____

Name _____

1. Read the following dialogue:

"Look at that!" _____.

"What do you think it is?" _____.

"I don't know, but look at it," _____.

"I've never seen anything like it," _____.

2. Now, add narration to the dialogue. Remember, narration is a phrase added to dialogue that helps the reader know who is speaking.

Example: "Look at that!" Lucy shouted.

Extra Practice: Please try the same exercise again using the following dialogue:

"How much do you think this comic book costs?" _____.

"I'm not sure, but it's very rare," _____.

"We should ask the cashier," _____.

"Good idea. I bet she would know," _____.

 CA W 1.0 Writing Strategies

Name _____

Some words have a pattern with a syllable break between two vowels. This is called the **V/V pattern**. The word *fuel,* for example, has a syllable break between the vowel *u* and the vowel *e*. This pattern is also found in words with more than two syllables, such as the word *idea*. Idea is a three syllable word: *i/de/a*.
A syllable that ends in a vowel is an **open syllable**.

Underline the words below that have a V/V pattern. Then draw a line dividing the two vowels in each underlined word to show where the V/V pattern is found.

diary _____

piano _____

minus _____

meteor _____

poet _____

riot _____

valley _____

casual _____

about _____

rodeo _____

closet _____

radio _____

fluid _____

hoarse _____

diameter _____

ruin _____

patriot _____

trial _____

diet _____

meander _____

cruel _____

fought _____

genuine _____

without _____

© Macmillan/McGraw-Hill

Name _____

A. Select the correct word from the choices in parentheses. Then write the correct word on the line provided.

1. The princess (descended / described) the stairs to meet the prince in the hall. _____

2. No princess was willing to (autograph / accompany) Prince Vincent down the aisle. _____

3. If the prince did not marry, the king would (despair / dismiss) him from the kingdom. _____

4. Prince Vincent was in (despair / delight), and his future looked hopeless.

_____

5. He thought he might have to (seek / sack) a wife in another land.

_____

6. The queen welcomed the princess as her guest and served her (delicacies / intentions) from different nations. _____

7. The prince told the queen about his (decorations / intentions) to marry the princess. _____

8. The princess (dismissed / consented) to his proposal, and they lived happily ever after. _____

B. Write two sentences that each includes one vocabulary word. Underline the vocabulary words you used.

9. _____

_____

10. _____

_____

© Macmillan/McGraw-Hill

 R 1.0 Word Analysis, Fluency, and Systematic Vocabulary Development

The **sequence** of events in a story is the order in which things happen. Determining the **chronological order** of events can help you summarize the action of a story.

Place the correct number for the chronological order of events in the left column next to the event described in the right column.

After Alexi spared the life of the Golden Mare, the horse became devoted to Alexi. Alexi became a huntsman for the Tsar. As his first order of business, Alexi captured the Firebird. Next, he asked Alexi to find Yelena the Fair so she could become his wife. Alexi persuaded Yelena to meet the Tsar. After Yelena discovered the Tsar's intention, she told the Tsar she would not get married without her grandmother's ring. The Golden Mare volunteered to fetch the ring from the lake. Yelena convinced the Tsar that she would turn a pot of water into a fountain of youth for him. The Tsar decided to test the water by having Alexi thrown in. Alexi survived and came out of the water with the ring. The Tsar was convinced that his youth would be restored, but he became an infant instead. Since he was too young to rule, Alexi became the Tsar and married Yelena. Alexi released the Firebird and the Golden Mare.

Order	Events from *The Golden Mare, the Firebird, and the Magic Ring*
	Alexi becomes a huntsman for the Tsar and captures the Firebird.
	Alexi spares the life of the Golden Mare, and the horse devotes her life to him.
	Yelena follows Alexi to meet the Tsar.
	Alexi is thrown into the cauldron of boiling water and survives.
	Alexi becomes Tsar and releases the Golden Mare.
	The Golden Mare volunteers to fetch Yelena's magic ring.

CA **R 2.2** Analyze text that is organized in sequential or chronological order.

The Golden Mare, the Firebird, and the Magic Ring • Grade 5/Unit 3

145

Name _____

**As you read *The Golden Mare, the Firebird, and the Magic Ring*, fill
in the Sequence Chart.**

Event

⬇

⬇

⬇

How does the information you wrote in this Sequence Chart help you
summarize *The Golden Mare, the Firebird, and the Magic Ring*?

R 2.2 Analyze text that is organized in sequential
or chronological order.

As I read, I will pay attention to intonation and phrasing.

	Once upon a time, a really, really long time ago, there lived
12	a beautiful, kind-hearted girl named Katharine. You would
21	have thought that such a lovely girl would be happy. But she
33	was not. She was sad and terribly lonely.
41	For you see (as is to be expected in a story like this),
54	Katharine's life was filled with sorrow. Her mother died
63	when she was young. Her father brought her to live with her
75	Aunt Mara and cousins Melina and Ursula while he went off
86	to fight for the king. Her father loved Katharine dearly and
97	promised to return for her as soon as possible, but that
108	promise was made many years ago.
114	Over the years, Katharine's cousins grew to hate her. They
124	knew that Katharine was kinder and more beautiful than they
134	were. Each day Melina and Ursula were meaner. They
143	ordered her around. Katharine was truly miserable.
150	So what did Katharine do all day? She did everything!
160	Inside she cooked and cleaned. Outside she planted, weeded,
169	and harvested the garden, fed the animals, cleaned the barn,
179	collected the eggs, and milked the cow. 186

Comprehension Check

1. Why was Katharine miserable? **Plot Development**

2. Why were Ursula and Melina cruel to Katharine? **Plot Development**

	Words Read	−	Number of Errors	=	Words Correct Score
First Read		−		=	
Second Read		−		=	

© Macmillan/McGraw-Hill

CA **R 1.1** Read aloud narrative and expository text fluently and accurately and with appropriate pacing, **intonation**, and expression.

The Golden Mare, the Firebird, and
the Magic Ring • **Grade 5/Unit 3**

Name _____

A **Venn diagram** compares two things. Differences are written in the left and right circles. Similarities are written where the circles overlap.

A. Read the summary of *Cinderella*, and fill in the Venn diagram.

Cinderella

Cinderella is a household servant with an evil stepmother, evil stepsisters, and a fairy godmother. She loses a slipper at a ball, and the prince searches the kingdom for the woman to whom it belongs. Cinderella and the prince get married and live happily ever after.

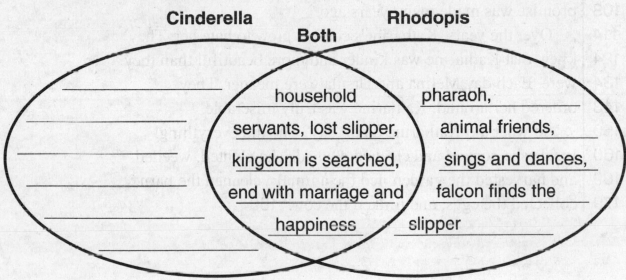

B. Read the completed Venn diagram and write a summary of *Rhodopis*.

Rhodopis

_____

_____

_____

_____

_____

_____

R 2.1 Understand how text features (e.g., format, graphics, sequence, diagrams, illustrations, charts, maps) make information accessible and usable.

© Macmillan/McGraw-Hill

Name _____

Homophones are two or more words that sound the same but have different spellings and different meanings.

A. Circle the word that makes sense in each sentence.

1. Most fairy tales are stories that you have (herd / **heard**) before.

2. The hero often must race to complete a task in just one (**hour** / our).

3. In some stories, people try to (by / **buy**) happiness with jewels or gold.

4. My baseball team (one / **won**) the game.

B. Write a word from the box next to each word below to make pairs of homophones. Then write a sentence using one of the homophones in each pair.

pear	flower	course	hear

5. here ___hear___

   I hear something around hear

6. coarse ___course___

   _____

7. pair ___pear___

   I see a pair of shoe and pear on the table

8. flour ___flower___

   I ve flour to make a cake, the cake smell like flower.

© Macmillan/McGraw-Hill

Name _____

Using the Word Study Steps

1. LOOK at the word.

2. SAY the word aloud.

3. STUDY the letters in the word.

4. WRITE the word.

5. CHECK the word.
Did you spell the word right?
If not, go back to step 1.

A. Fill-Ins

Fill in the missing letters of each word to form a spelling word.

1. cas _____ _____ l

2. rod _____

3. rad _____ _____

4. p _____ _____ t

5. d _____ _____ meter

6. r _____ _____ n

7. vid _____ _____

8. p _____ _____ no

9. cr _____ _____ l

10. met _____ _____ r

11. gen _____ _____ ne

12. fl _____ _____ d

13. d _____ _____ ry

14. id _____ _____ s

15. patr _____ _____ t

16. f _____ _____ l

17. d _____ _____ t

18. r _____ _____ t

19. tr _____ _____ l

20. m _____ _____ nder

B. Reverse Alphabetical Order

Use the lines below to write the spelling words in reverse alphabetical order.

1. _____

2. _____

3. _____

4. _____

5. _____

6. _____

7. _____

8. _____

9. _____

10. _____

11. _____

12. _____

13. _____

14. _____

15. _____

16. _____

17. _____

18. _____

19. _____

20. _____

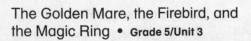 **LC 1.5** Spell roots, suffixes, prefixes, contractions, and syllable constructions correctly.

© Macmillan/McGraw-Hill

Name _____

A. Circle the misspelled words in the passage. Write the words correctly on the lines below.

Mrs. Esther Morris was a true patreot. In her time, she would have been called a genuen article. She was a fair judge. She didn't punish Ben Sheeks when he misbehaved during a tryial. There was no vidio when Mrs. Morris lived. There wasn't even radeo. I would have liked to see or hear her. I like many of her ideus.

1. _____   3. _____   5. _____

2. _____   4. _____   6. _____

B. Writing Activity

Suppose that you could write a letter to Mrs. Morris. What would you say about her ideas? How would you describe what voting is like today? Use the lines below to write your letter. Include four spelling words.

_____

_____

_____

_____

_____

_____

_____

_____

_____

_____

_____

CA **LC 1.5** Spell roots, suffixes, prefixes, contractions, and syllable constructions correctly.

Name _____

- A verb in the **past tense** tells about an action that already happened.
- If a verb ends in *e,* drop the *e* before adding *-ed*: **hoped.**
- If a verb ends in one vowel and one consonant, double the consonant before adding *-ed*: **omitted**.
- If a verb ends in a consonant and *y,* change *y* to *i* before adding *-ed*: **carried**.
- A verb in the **future tense** tells about an action that is going to happen. To write about the future, use the word *will* in front of the verb.

collect	**change**	**remember**	**invite**
pass	**gain**	**serve**	**vote**

A. Complete each sentence with the past tense of one of the verbs in the box above.

1. Both men and women _____ in elections.

2. Women in Wyoming _____ the right to vote.

3. She _____ stones to build a memorial.

4. The government _____ the Constitution.

B. Complete each sentence with the future tense of one of the verbs in the box above.

5. Much time _____ before the Constitution changes again.

6. Many people _____ Esther Morris forever.

7. The mayor of South Pass City _____ the citizens to a dedication ceremony.

8. Esther Morris _____ as a judge in South Pass City.

LC 1.0 Written and Oral English Language Conventions

Name _____

- A verb in the **present tense** tells what is happening now.
- A verb in the **past tense** tells about an action that already happened.
- A verb in the **future tense** tells about an action that is going to happen.

Rewrite the following passage. Change the tense or spelling of incorrect verbs. Correct errors in capitalization.

Esther morris traveleded by carriage to South pass city, When she arrived, she thought, "I will paid a call on Colonel William Bright." colonel Bright was busy getting his beard trimmed, so she wait outside of the barber shop.

After some time will pass, Mr. Benjamin Sheeks walked by and asked her if she thought South Pass City was a pleasant place to visit. Esther say that her vote was yes to that question. Mr. Sheeks was surprise by her reply. He said that women were not allowed to vote. Esther will smile, and asked him why he had asked her the question if he thought she couldn't have an opinion.

_____

_____

_____

_____

_____

_____

_____

_____

_____

Name _____

1. Read the following dialogue:

"Wow!" shouted Tom.

"This is the best thing I've ever done!"

"I can't believe we never tried this before!" Tom yelled.

"When we're done, lets go again!" Sara shouted.

2. Now, rewrite these sentences to show:

   a. What Sara and Tom are doing

   b. Where they are

   c. What actions they are making

Example: "Wow!" shouted Tom, looking back at Sara as he slid down the watery slide.

_____

_____

_____

_____

_____

_____

_____

_____

Extra Practice: Try the exercise again with the following dialogue:

"This is delicious!" Mimi exclaimed.

"I've never had anything quite like it," Aaron added.

"What do you think it's made of?" asked Mimi.

"Not sure, but it tastes a little like cherries," observed Aaron.

© Macmillan/McGraw-Hill

Name _____

Every word has one or more syllables, and every syllable contains one vowel sound. Some vowel sounds are spelled with two letters. These letters form a **vowel team**. The two letters in each vowel team appear in the same syllable.

Often in vowel teams, the first vowel is long, and the second vowel is silent. When you read a syllable that contains a vowel team, try the long sound first. If the word does not sound right, then try another vowel sound.

Divide each word into syllables. Then underline the vowel team in each word. The first one has been done for you.

lean|ing

1. raining

2. grounded

3. Sunday

4. eighty

5. floated

6. bookshelf

7. meanest

8. soapbox

9. snowstorm

10. potpie

A. From each pair of words in parentheses, circle the one that best completes the sentence. Then write the correct word on the line provided.

Some stories are told with words; others are told with music. Ballads

are songs that tell a story. For hundreds of years, singers have shared

these songs with people in nearby towns and around the (sphere/globe)

1. _____. Sad ballads, such as "Oh, Shenandoah,"

(remain/reveal) 2. _____ the troubles of people who

lived centuries ago. (Amusing/Amazing) 3. _____

ballads, such as "On Top of Spaghetti," tell stories that make us laugh. By

singing ballads, we can (preserve/prepare) 4. _____ our

favorite stories and pass them along to future (generations/geographies)

5. _____.

B. Write new sentences for three of the vocabulary words that you circled above. Underline the vocabulary word.

6. _____

7. _____

8. _____

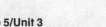

CA R 1.0 Word Analysis, Fluency, and Systematic Vocabulary Development

© Macmillan/McGraw-Hill

Name _____

When you **compare** information, you tell how two or more things are alike. When you **contrast** information, you tell how two or more things are different. Often, authors use signal words to show whether they are comparing or contrasting.

Words for Comparing

like   too
both   also
and

Words for Contrasting

unlike
but
however

Read the story. Circle four signal words. Then answer the questions, using complete sentences.

"When can I go home?" wondered Terrance. He had been at Grandma's house for two hours and he was already bored. Terrance lived in the city, but Grandma lived in the country. At home, Terrance could walk to the ball field by himself. But here, Grandma had to drive him everywhere. Unlike Terrance, Grandma didn't have a computer. She didn't even have a TV! Terrance was supposed to stay at Grandma's for a month; he worried that it would feel like a year.

Then Grandma said, "I need your help with something." She showed Terrance a big plastic box full of old baseball cards. Terrance could see that he and Grandma were both big baseball fans. As they started to sort the cards, Grandma told Terrance interesting stories about the players. Maybe summer at Grandma's would be fun after all!

1. What is one way that Terence and Grandma are different?

   Terrance live in city, but Grandma lived
   in the country.

2. What is one way that Terence and Grandma are the same?

   Terrance and Grandma didt have a computer

Name _____

As you read *Tricky Tales*, fill in the Venn Diagram.

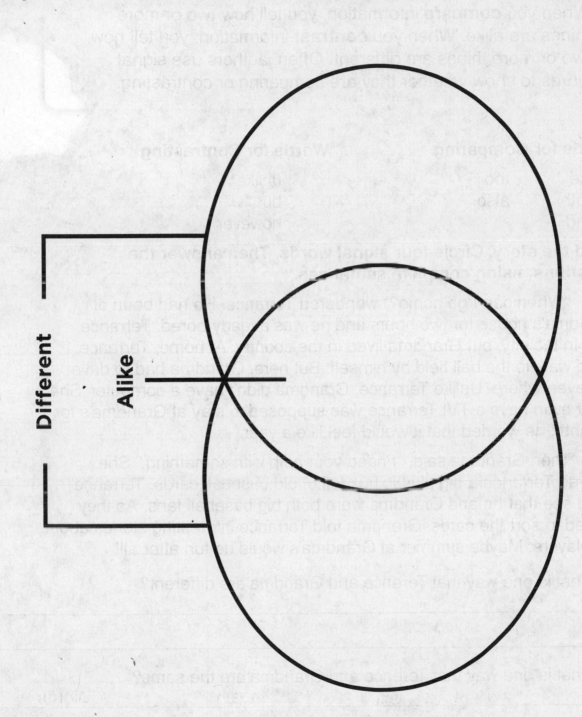

Different

Alike

How does the information you wrote in this Venn Diagram help you
compare and contrast the stories in *Tricky Tales*?

CA **R 2.0** Reading Comprehension (Focus on Informational Materials)

Name _____Kaig_____

As I read, I will pay attention to phrasing.

	"It's finally here!" I said to myself as I got off the school
13	bus that Friday afternoon. "And it's going to be great!"
23	I had been patient. I'd waited and waited for the big
34	family party. It was just one day away. From all over the city
47	and even as far away as Baltimore, my family was meeting
58	at our house for a cookout supper Saturday night. My older
69	sister, Mai, was excited, too. She had promised to decorate our
80	backyard and even string little lights all over the trees and
91	bushes. We'd start today, and then finish up tomorrow
100	morning before her big soccer game. I never missed Mai's
110	soccer games. She and her team were the city champions,
120	and their games were really fun to watch.
128	But now it was time to decorate the yard. 137

Comprehension Check

1. Why is the narrator excited? **Cause and Effect**

2. What is Mai's responsibility for the party? **Plot Development**

	Words Read	–	Number of Errors	=	Words Correct Score
First Read		–		=	
Second Read		–		=	

R 1.1 Read aloud narrative and expository text fluently and accurately and with appropriate pacing, intonation, and expression.

Name _____

Using an **outline** can help you group facts and organize information while you study. First **skim**, or quickly read, the article. Next **scan**, or look carefully, for the titles, headings, and key vocabulary words of the article. Then write your notes in an outline.

Look at the outline below. Then answer the questions.

Environmental Dangers

I. Global warming

   A. Pollution is making it inevitable that ice at Earth's poles will melt.

   B. Coastlines and weather will change.

II. Damage to the ozone layer

   A. Ozone gas protects us from the sun.

   B. Pollution has caused the amount of ozone to decrease.

III. Acid rain

   A. Pollution from fossil fuels mixes with rain.

   B. Acid rain can harm trees, wildlife, and buildings.

1. What sort of information follows the Roman numerals? _____

_____

_____

2. What sort of information follows the capital letters? _____

_____

_____

© Macmillan/McGraw-Hill

 R 2.0 Reading Comprehension (Focus on Informational Materials)

Name _____

Compare/Contrast Writing Frame

A. Summarize *Tricky Tales*. Use the Compare/Contrast Writing Frame below.

Both Robert Greygrass and Tchin are the **same** in some ways. They are the
same because _____

_____

_____

_____.

However, in other ways Robert Greygrass and Tchin are **different**. They are
different because _____

_____

_____

_____.

So, Robert Greygrass and Tchin have both **similarities** and **differences**.

**B. Rewrite the completed summary on another sheet of paper. Keep it as
a model for writing a summary of an article or selection using this text
structure.**

 R 2.0 Reading Comprehension

Name _____

Homographs are words that are spelled the same way but
have different meanings and may have different pronunciations.

**A. Read each sentence. Circle the definition of the underlined word
as it is used in the sentence.**

1. Be careful not to <u>jam</u> your finger in the door.

   a. fruit spread   **b.** press or squeeze

2. The moral of the story is to be <u>kind</u> to others.

   a. friendly and helpful   **b.** the same type

3. We planted the carrots in a <u>row</u>.

   a. line   **b.** use oars to move a boat

4. <u>Close</u> the door so the dog does not run out.

   a. near   **b.** shut

5. I will <u>lead</u> my dog to the park on Sunday.

   a. a type of metal   **b.** show the way

**B. Read the definitions for each pair of homographs. Then write a
sentence using one of the homographs in the pair.**

6. palm

   a. inside of a hand   **b.** kind of tree

   _____

7. rest

   a. sleep   **b.** what is left

   _____

8. present

   a. here; not gone   **b.** a gift

   _____

 R 1.3 Understand and explain frequently used synonyms, antonyms,
and homographs.

Name _____

Using the Word Study Steps

1. LOOK at the word.

2. SAY the word aloud.

3. STUDY the letters in the word.

4. WRITE the word.

5. CHECK the word.

Did you spell the word right?

If not, go back to step 1.

A. Fill in the missing letters of each word to form a spelling word.

1. l___ ___yer

2. gr___ ___chy

3. r___ ___ghness

4. appl___ ___se

5. f___ ___tprint

6. entert___ ___n

7. c___ ___stal

8. b___ ___ndary

9. gr___ ___nup

10. l___ ___ghter

11. f___ ___cet

12. c___ ___tion

13. alth___ ___gh

14. enc___ ___nter

15. app___ ___nt

16. fl___ ___less

17. bl___ ___chers

18. f___ ___rground

19. d___ ___bting

20. s___ ___thern

B. Use the lines below to write the spelling words in alphabetical order.

1. _____   6. _____   11. _____   16. _____

2. _____   7. _____   12. _____   17. _____

3. _____   8. _____   13. _____   18. _____

4. _____   9. _____   14. _____   19. _____

5. _____   10. _____   15. _____   20. _____

© Macmillan/McGraw-Hill

LC 1.5 Spell roots, suffixes, prefixes, contractions, and **syllable constructions** correctly.

Name _____

A. Circle the misspelled words in the passage. Write the words correctly on the lines below.

Each year, storytellers from around the United States come to the suothern state of Tennessee for the National Storytelling Festival. Storytellers perform in giant tents and entertane audiences who sit in bleechers. These are the best storytellers in the country, and the tales they tell are flauless. Delighted audiences fill the tents with lafter and applaus.

1. _____   3. _____   5. _____

2. _____   4. _____   6. _____

B. Writing Activity

Suppose that you were asked to tell a story in a storytelling festival. What story would you tell? Write a story, using four spelling words.

_____

_____

_____

_____

_____

_____

_____

_____

_____

_____

_____

_____

 LC 1.5 Spell roots, suffixes, prefixes, contractions, and **syllable constructions** correctly.

© Macmillan/McGraw-Hill

Name _____

- Forms of *be* (*is, are, am, was,* and *were*) can be used as **helping verbs**.
- Make sure that the helping verb agrees with the subject. Use *is* and *was* with a singular subject. Use *are* and *were* with a plural subject or *you*. Use *am* or *was* with *I*.

Choose a form of *be* as a helping verb to complete each sentence.

1. The students _____ working to create a safer and more healthful environment.

2. I _____ trying to recycle all of my cans and bottles.

3. The world _____ risking the danger of global warming.

4. Acid rain _____ harming trees and wild animals.

5. Environmental organizations _____ growing around the world.

6. The result _____ appearing as an improvement in living standards.

7. Years ago, scientists _____ becoming concerned about the effects of technology.

8. McDougald's class _____ sending out a message about wilderness responsibility.

9. I _____ doing my part to protect the forests of America.

10. Parks _____ becoming beautiful places to picnic.

Name _____

- The **main verb** in a sentence shows what the subject does or is.
- A **helping verb** helps the main verb show an action or make a statement.

Rewrite the following passage. Change the helping verbs to match the subject. Add commas where necessary.

According to many scientists around the world, the environment are getting worse. Global warming am a serious threat to healthy living. I were a college student in southern Ohio. I has researched the subject, and I had come to the conclusion that we need to decrease pollution recycle our cans and bottles and conserve our natural resources. The time have come to take more responsibility for our actions.

I have begun an environmental organization called Help Us Breathe. Our group am working to get more people to take a train or bus to work. We also was trying to educate people on the importance of recycling.

_____

_____

_____

_____

_____

_____

_____

_____

_____

_____

_____

Name _____

Writing Rubric

4 Excellent	3 Good	2 Fair	1 Unsatisfactory
Ideas and Content/ Genre	Ideas and Content/ Genre	Ideas and Content/ Genre	Ideas and Content/ Genre
Organization and Focus	Organization and Focus	Organization and Focus	Organization and Focus
Sentence Structure/ Fluency	Sentence Structure/ Fluency	Sentence Structure/ Fluency	Sentence Structure/ Fluency
Conventions	Conventions	Conventions	Conventions
Word Choice	Word Choice	Word Choice	Word Choice
Voice	Voice	Voice	Voice
Presentation	Presentation	Presentation	Presentation

© Macmillan/McGraw-Hill

Name _____

Many words end in a consonant and the letters *le*. In those words, the consonant and the letters *le* form the last syllable.

If the syllable before the last syllable ends in a vowel, it is an open syllable and has a long vowel sound. If the syllable before the last syllable ends with a consonant, it is a closed syllable and has a short vowel sound.

Read each consonant + *le* word below. Put a slash through the word to separate the syllables. Then look at the first syllable. If it is an open syllable, write *O* after the word. If it is a closed syllable, write *C* after the word.

1. stable _____

2. maple _____

3. candle _____

4. gentle _____

5. single _____

6. bubble _____

7. fable _____

8. apple _____

9. eagle _____

10. little _____

 R 1.0 Word Analysis, Fluency, and Systematic Vocabulary Development

Name _____

As you read *Blancaflor*, fill in the Theme Chart.

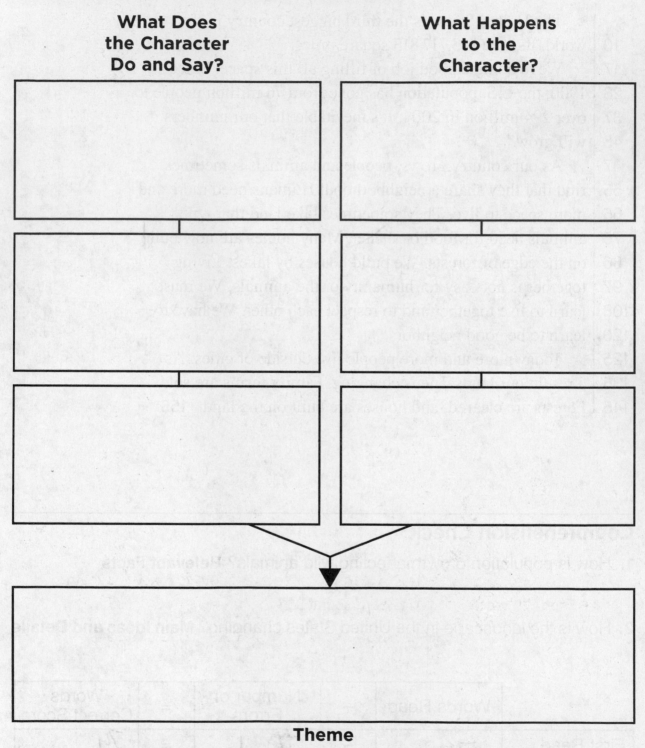

**What Does
the Character
Do and Say?**

**What Happens
to the
Character?**

Theme

How does the information you wrote in the Theme Chart help you
understand the theme of *Blancaflor*?

© Macmillan/McGraw-Hill

R 3.4 Understand that *theme* refers to the meaning or moral of a
selection and recognize themes (whether implied or stated directly)
in sample works.

Name _____

As I read, I will pay attention to pacing.

10	The United States is the third biggest country in the world. Its area is 3,717,813 square miles.
17	We're doing a good job of filling all this space. Since
28	1900, the U.S. population has gone from 76 million people to
37	over 294 million in 2004. It's inevitable that our numbers
45	will grow.
47	As our country grows, people and animals sometimes
55	find that they share a neighborhood! Humans need more and
65	more space to live. They sometimes take land that wild
75	animals need for food or shelter. Many homes are now built
86	on the edge of forests. We build houses by lakes. Living
97	together is not easy for humanity or the animals. We must
108	learn to live together and to respect each other. We have to
120	learn to be good neighbors.
125	Today more and more people live outside of cities. As
135	a result, our landscape is changing. Family farms are sold.
145	Forests are cleared, and houses are built on the land. 155

Comprehension Check

1. How is population growth affecting wild animals? **Relevant Facts**

Since 1900, the U.S. population has gone from 76 million to over 294 million in 2004.

2. How is the landscape in the United States changing? **Main Ideas and Details**

More and More people live outside of cities.

	Words Read	−	Number of Errors	=	Words Correct Score
First Read	75	−	1	=	74
Second Read		−		=	

CA **R 1.1** Read aloud narrative and expository text fluently and accurately and with appropriate pacing, intonation, and expression.

Name _____

A **map** is a drawing of an area that shows features such as towns, roads, rivers, and lakes.

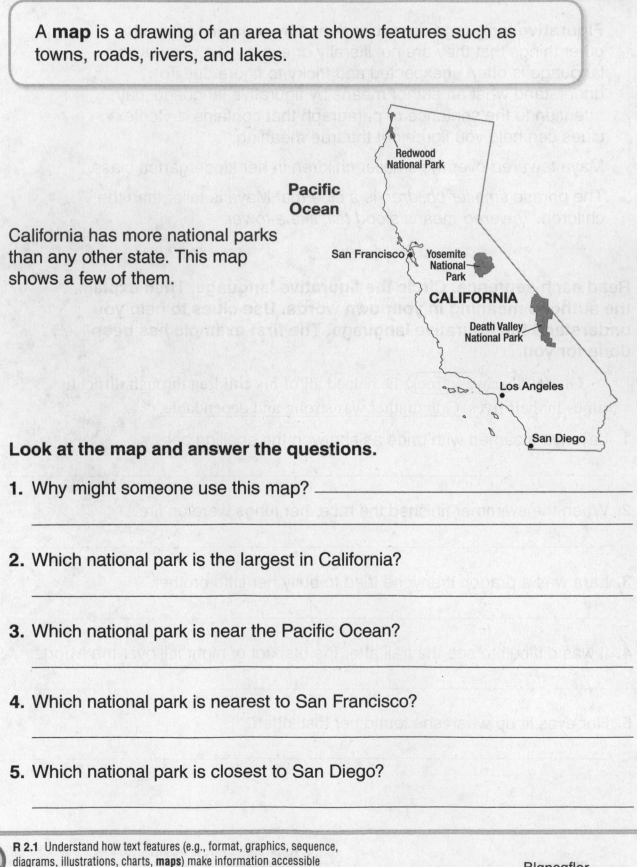

California has more national parks than any other state. This map shows a few of them.

Look at the map and answer the questions.

1. Why might someone use this map? _____

_____

2. Which national park is the largest in California?

_____

3. Which national park is near the Pacific Ocean?

_____

4. Which national park is nearest to San Francisco?

_____

5. Which national park is closest to San Diego?

_____

© Macmillan/McGraw-Hill

CA R 2.1 Understand how text features (e.g., format, graphics, sequence, diagrams, illustrations, charts, **maps**) make information accessible and usable.

Figurative language describes things by comparing them to other things that they are not literally or exactly like. Figurative language is often unexpected and tricky to figure out. To understand what an author means by figurative language, pay attention to the sentence or paragraph that contains it. Context clues can help you figure out the true meaning.

Maya *towered* over the smaller children in her kindergarten class.

The phrase *smaller children* is a clue that Maya is taller than the children. *Towered* means *stood tall, like a tower.*

Read each sentence. Circle the figurative language. Then explain the author's meaning in your own words. Use clues to help you understand the figurative language. The first example has been done for you.

Grandfather (was a rock); he helped all of his children through difficult times in their lives. Grandfather was strong and dependable.

1. LaTonya gleamed with pride as she won the spelling bee.

_____

2. When the swimmer finished the race, her lungs were on fire.

_____

3. Lara was a dragon if anyone tried to bully her little brother.

_____

4. It was difficult to see the trail after the blanket of night fell over the woods.

_____

5. Her eyes lit up when she found her lost kitten.

_____

© Macmillan/McGraw-Hill

 CA **R 1.5** Understand and explain the figurative and metaphorical use of words in context.

Name _____

Using the Word Study Steps

1. LOOK at the word.
2. SAY the word aloud.
3. STUDY the letters in the word.

4. WRITE the word.
5. CHECK the word.
   Did you spell the word right?
   If not, go back to step 1.

Fill-Ins

A. Fill in the missing letters of each word to form a spelling word.

1. stum _____ _____ _____
2. roy _____ _____
3. ket _____ _____ _____
4. hospi _____ _____ _____
5. sam _____ _____ _____
6. cat _____ _____ _____
7. crip _____ _____ _____
8. nob _____ _____
9. tab _____ _____
10. eag _____ _____

11. journ _____ _____
12. beet _____ _____
13. sad _____ _____ _____
14. med _____ _____
15. stab _____ _____
16. leg _____ _____
17. sever _____ _____
18. terrib _____ _____
19. voc _____ _____
20. lab _____ _____

B. Write the Words

Use the lines below to practice writing the spelling words.

1. _____
2. _____
3. _____
4. _____
5. _____

6. _____
7. _____
8. _____
9. _____
10. _____

11. _____
12. _____
13. _____
14. _____
15. _____

16. _____
17. _____
18. _____
19. _____
20. _____

 LC 1.5 Spell roots, suffixes, prefixes, contractions, and **syllable constructions** correctly.

Name _____

A. Circle the misspelled words in this passage. Write the words correctly on the lines below.

     Out in the barn, Eli found a leather bag. Inside was an old book. On the cover was a lable: "Abe Jefferson, 1924." Eli could see that it was a jurnle that had belonged to his great-grandfather when he was just a boy. Eli read the first entry: "This morning, I put the sadell on Lightning and went out to round up the catel. In the distance, I could hear a terribal crash of thunder. Severall minutes later, I saw the sky turn a greenish yellow. I wondered if a tornado was coming…."

     Eli turned the page. The rest of the book was empty. Eli put the journal in the bag and headed back to the house. Maybe his grandmother would know the end of the story.

1. _____   3. _____   5. _____

2. _____   4. _____   6. _____

B. Writing Activity

Write an ending to the journal entry, using four spelling words.

_____

_____

_____

_____

_____

_____

_____

_____

 LC 1.5 Spell roots, suffixes, prefixes, contractions, and **syllable constructions** correctly.

Name _____

> • A **linking verb** links the subject of a sentence to a noun or an adjective in the predicate.
> • The noun that follows a linking verb renames or identifies the subject.
> • The adjective that follows a linking verb describes the subject.

A. Read each sentence. Underline the word that is connected to the subject by a linking verb.

1. The water pump is broken.

2. My grandmother is worried about the baobab trees.

3. I felt proud of my grandmother's accomplishment.

4. The village was concerned about the lack of water.

5. People in our village seem very thankful for my grandmother's generosity.

B. Complete each sentence with a linking verb. Then underline the word that names or describes the subject.

6. The desert _____ a dry, hot landscape.

7. I _____ thankful for the baobab trees.

8. All of the villagers _____ fascinated with new technology.

9. I _____ a little nervous when no water spilled from the pump.

10. Water _____ better from the baobab tree.

11. The villagers say that she _____ a mysterious old woman.

12. The desert _____ filled with water someday.

Name _____

- A **linking verb** does not show action. A linking verb shows a state of being or states a condition.
- A linking verb links the subject of a sentence to a noun or an adjective in the predicate.
- The noun that follows a linking verb renames or identifies the subject.

Rewrite the passage. Use the correct verb forms.

The time has come for me to make my journey into the desert. I is only 18. But, all children my age am required to make the journey to be accepted as adult members of the community. The village chief told me that it were very important to take plenty of water and materials to build a tent.

The mission seem long and hard. I tastes the fresh water from my canteen, and the sun feel too hot to bear. I travel many days and many nights.

After seven days, I return home with relief. As I arrive back at my village, the villagers appears so proud of me.

_____

_____

_____

_____

_____

_____

_____

_____

_____

_____

_____

 LC 1.0 Written and Oral English Language Conventions

Name _____

Read the following sentence:

Monique felt nervous when she got on the bus.

Now, write 2–3 sentences that show how Monique feels. You can use descriptive details, dialogue, and strong verbs.

Example: Monique was looking down, but she could feel everyone's eyes on her. Her stomach was in knots as she rushed down the aisle trying to find an empty seat.

_____

_____

_____

_____

_____

_____

_____

_____

_____

_____

_____

_____

_____

_____

Extra Practice: Do the same exercise again, using the following sentence.

Jonah was disappointed that he lost the tennis match.

Name _____

The **schwa-r** sound is a vowel sound often found in unaccented syllables. The three most common spellings for words that end in the /ər/ sound include *ar*, *er*, and *or*.

A. Write the correct spelling for the final /ər sound/: *ar, er, or.*

1. spid ____ ____

2. broth ____ ____

3. coll ____ ____

4. doll ____ ____

5. jogg ____ ____

6. schol ____ ____

7. err ____ ____

8. vap ____ ____

9. equat ____ ____

10. peddl ____ ____

11. barb ____ ____

12. generat ____ ____

B. Write a paragraph using at least six words from the list above. Make sure you underline each word.

_____

_____

_____

_____

_____

_____

_____

_____

_____

_____

 CA R 1.0 Word Analysis, Fluency, and Systematic Vocabulary Development

Name _____

enlisted	location	shield	reservation
invasion	corridor	transmission	creased

A. Choose a vocabulary word from the box to complete each sentence.

1. Grandfather said that his belief was his _____ from danger and kept him safe during the war.

2. The _____ of the class for the code talkers was secret.

3. They used radios for the _____ of information.

4. We spoke both Navajo and English when we lived on the

   _____.

5. The _____ that led to the code talkers' classroom was long and narrow.

6. My grandfather's face was _____ from years of smiling and laughing.

7. Grandfather explained why he had _____ in the army when he was a young man.

8. The soldiers planned an _____ of enemy land.

B. Write two sentences, each using a vocabulary word.

9. _____

   _____

10. _____

    _____

> The **author's perspective** is his or her opinion about the topic.
> The perspective affects how a story is written because the author
> chooses words and a tone that show his or her opinions, feelings,
> and beliefs.

Read each passage. Then answer the questions.

John raced up the trail, sending pebbles skidding behind him. When he reached his favorite hiding place, he fell to the ground out of breath. The river, full of late-summer rain, looked like a silver thread winding through his grandfather's farmland. They would be looking for him, but he was never coming down.

1. Explain the author's perspective on John's feelings.

_____

_____

2. What is the author's opinion about nature? How do you know?

_____

_____

His grandfather lifted him gently onto the horse. "The answer to that is in the code," he said. "The code name for America was 'Our Mother.' You fight for what you love. You fight for what is yours."

3. Explain how the author feels about the grandfather.

_____

_____

_____

4. What do you think the author's opinion is on protecting the United States?

_____

_____

© Macmillan/McGraw-Hill

 R 2.0 Reading Comprehension

Name _____

As you read *The Unbreakable Code*, fill in the Author's Perspective Chart.

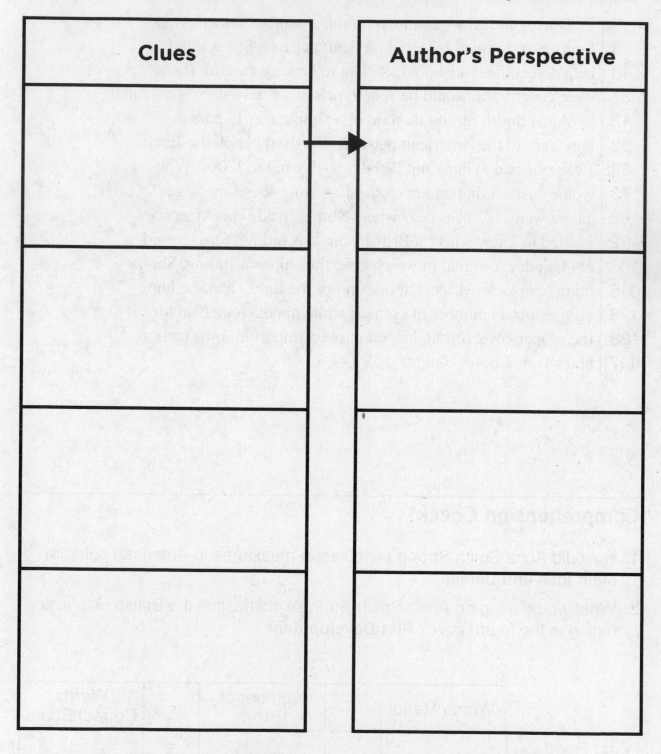

Clues	Author's Perspective

How does the information you wrote in the Author's Perspective Chart help you generate questions about *The Unbreakable Code*?

Name _____

As I read, I will pay attention to intonation and phrasing.

	During the American Revolution, a woman named Anna
8	Smith Strong spied for the American patriots. She wanted to
18	help defeat the British, but she had to be very careful. If she
31	were caught, she would be sent to prison, or maybe even executed.
43	Anna Smith Strong thought of a simple way to pass
53	messages to the American patriots. She used her clothesline!
62	Everyone had to hang out laundry to dry in the 1700s. Who
73	would suspect that on her clothesline hung secret messages?
82	There were six coves near where Strong lived. The Americans
92	needed to know where a British ship was hiding. Strong used
103	her laundry to signal in which cove the ship was hiding. She
115	hung her black petticoat at one end of the line. Then she hung
128	up the correct number of creased white handkerchiefs to identify
138	the proper cove. Strong helped pass on important information—
147	and she was never caught. 152

Comprehension Check

1. How did Anna Smith Strong send secret messages to American patriots? **Main Idea and Details**

2. What would hang on Anna Smith Strong's clothesline if a British ship was hiding in the fourth cove? **Plot Development**

	Words Read	–	Number of Errors	=	Words Correct Score
First Read		–		=	
Second Read		–		=	

R 1.1 Read aloud narrative and expository text fluently and accurately and with appropriate pacing, intonation, and expression.

Name _____

In poetry, **consonance** is the repetition of final consonant sounds in a series of words. **Symbolism** is the use of a concrete object to represent an abstract idea.

Read each cinquain below and then answer the questions.

Brother   1
Tell us about   2
Fellow brave and fearless   3
Navajo saved country and lives   4
And hope.   5

1. Which word shows consonance with *fearless* in line 3? _____

2. How could line 5 be rewritten to continue the consonance in line 4?

_____

Warning   1
Coding of words   2
In the puzzle of war   3
"Iron Fish" waiting underwater   4
Lives saved.   5

3. Which words in lines 3 and 4 show consonance? _____

4. The words "Iron Fish" probably symbolize which wartime vehicle?

_____

5. Why might using a symbol in a poem interest the reader more than simply

stating what the symbol represents? _____

_____

_____

R 2.0 Reading Comprehension
R 3.5 Describe the function and effect of common literary devices
(e.g., imagery, metaphor, **symbolism**).

The Unbreakable Code
Grade 5/Unit 3   185

Name _____

You can often figure out what an unfamiliar word is by using **context clues**, which you can find by looking at other words in the sentence or in surrounding sentences.

Circle all the context clues that help you define the underlined word in each sentence.

1. During the drills, we said the same code over and over. We hoped that by <u>repeating</u> the code many times, it would be easy to remember.

2. Henry heard the wind always. The noise of the wind in the canyons especially was <u>ceaseless</u>. Its sound never stopped.

3. The <u>fierceness</u> of the Navajo Marines was well known. They were strong, brave, and powerful.

4. John felt <u>anxiety</u> about moving to Minnesota. He was nervous about living in a new place and worried about leaving.

5. Grandfather said that the code was a <u>triumph</u>. Each message was sent and received with success. Their goal had been reached!

6. Jen explained that only Navajos live on the <u>reservation</u>. The land is theirs to farm, protect, and enjoy.

7. Grandfather's face <u>wrinkled</u> as he laughed with his grandson. His cheeks scrunched up and lines appeared at the corners of his eyes.

8. When no rain fell, the leaves of Maria's favorite tree began to <u>wither</u>. They started to dry up and shrink.

© Macmillan/McGraw-Hill

 R 1.0 Word Analysis, Fluency, and Systematic Vocabulary Development

Name _____

Using the Word Study Steps

1. LOOK at the word.

2. SAY the word aloud.

3. STUDY the letters in the word.

4. WRITE the word.

5. CHECK the word.
   Did you spell the word right?
   If not, go back to step 1.

A. Find and Circle

Find and circle each of the spelling words in this puzzle. Words may read forward, backward, upward, downward, or diagonally.

```
R  R  E  T  A  R  C  I  P  R  O  F  E  S  S  O  R  S
C  E  E  R  R  O  R  N  B  J  K  H  X  S  G  R  R  R
K  R  D  T  T  N  W  J  V  O  I  M  M  Y  M  O  E  R
O  O  G  N  R  O  D  N  E  L  P  S  S  Z  S  I  V  A
E  B  O  R  A  D  I  R  E  C  T  O  R  S  D  A  R  L
Q  A  V  W  E  M  R  A  G  U  S  J  I  L  P  O  E  O
U  L  E  C  Q  D  M  H  J  C  O  C  O  O  X  O  C  H
A  W  R  R  U  Q  N  O  W  F  S  S  R  R  D  A  U  C
T  T  N  K  Z  X  X  U  C  S  H  A  T  T  E  R  A  S
O  M  O  D  P  S  S  Z  O  G  E  N  T  L  E  R  S  R
R  A  R  P  I  L  L  A  R  F  O  P  E  D  D  L  E  R
```

B. List the words below as you find them in the puzzle.

1. _____   11. _____

2. _____   12. _____

3. _____   13. _____

4. _____   14. _____

5. _____   15. _____

6. _____   16. _____

7. _____   17. _____

8. _____   18. _____

9. _____   19. _____

10. _____   20. _____

CA **LC 1.5** Spell roots, suffixes, prefixes, contractions, and syllable constructions correctly.

Name _____

A. Circle the misspelled words in the passage. Write the words correctly on the lines below.

Danny and Walter were sitting inside when the entire house began to shake. It felt as if the windows could shattur at any moment. Slowly, a mysterious vapur started pouring in from underneath the door. Walter almost dropped the scissers he was holding as the flying sauser knocked over a piller just outside the house. When they looked outside, there was a huge krater in the driveway.

1. _____   3. _____   5. _____

2. _____   4. _____   6. _____

B. Writing Activity

Write a paragraph about a game that you like to play. Use four spelling words in your paragraph.

_____

_____

_____

_____

_____

_____

_____

_____

_____

_____

_____

_____

_____

The Unbreakable Code
Grade 5/Unit 3
188

LC 1.5 Spell roots, suffixes, prefixes, contractions, and syllable constructions correctly.

© Macmillan/McGraw-Hill

Name _____ Chau Vo #24

- An **irregular verb** is a verb that does not use -ed to form the past tense.
- Some irregular verbs have special endings when used with the helping verbs *have*, *has*, or *had*.

Change the following verbs so that they can be used with the helping verb.

1. begin   had   _____

2. choose   have   _____

3. eat   has   _____

4. drink   had   _____

5. take   have   _____

6. get   has   _____

7. speak   had   _____

8. grow   has   _____

9. fly   have   _____

10. know   had   _____

Name ___Chau Vo #24___

- Be sure that verbs are in the correct form.
- Be sure that each sentence begins with a capital letter and ends with the correct punctuation mark.

Circle verbs that are in the incorrect form. Also, circle mistakes in capitalization and punctuation. Then rewrite the passage, adding commas where needed.

  Luther and i have always been great friends. We have do fun things together and have saw many crazy sights. Last Thursday we seen the craziest sight ever,

  We were walking down an alley when a space alien jumped out from behind a pile of tall smelly wet trash.

  The space alien was large blue, and plump, He moved toward us. He leaved slimy sludge on the ground when he walked, and he smelled like a dirty garbage can. when he got close to us, he standed up tall, stretch his four arms out and wrapped them around us. He gave us a quick, gentle, loving squeeze and then went back behind the pile of trash.

© Macmillan/McGraw-Hill

Name **Chau Vo #24**

Dissection Day
By Audrey Jackson

On February 4, 2005, first and second period in Mr. Shadow's class had to dissect a shark. Corey went to get it and returned to his group's table, carrying the shark like a sleeping baby. Talia told him, "Don't come next to me with that shark. Take your fishy child away from me." And he dumped it on the table right in front of her.

So Talia decided to get it over with. She would take care of it. "Pass me the scissors so I can slice and dice." She cut straight down on the left side and this yellow juice squirted out. It stunk. Everyone backed off but Jeanette. Talia watched Jeanette carefully—she saw her wrinkle her nose, and lean in to take a closer look.

"Pass me the other scissors," Jeannette demanded. "This looks like fun." Now Talia leaned in and together, Jeanette and Talia began slicing and cutting. It looked like they were unwrapping candy. Talia couldn't wait to see what was behind the next flap of skin.

Directions:

1. Read the excerpt above:

2. Answer the following questions in your journal:

    a. What emotions does Talia feel at the beginning of her shark dissection experience and how do you know?

    b. What emotions does Talia feel at the end of her shark dissection experience and how do you know?

    c. Where do you think the climax of the story is? Hint—what happens just before we see a change?

Name _____ ~~Chan Vo #24~~

Many words have unaccented final syllables. Some of these words end with the /əl/ sound, as you hear in the word ***bottle***. Other words have a final /ən/ sound, as you hear in the word ***sharpen***. The final /əl/ sound may be spelled as *-el*, *-le*, *-il*, or *-al*. The final /ən/ sound may be spelled as *-en*, *-in*, *-an*, *-on*, or *-ain*.

Circle the word in each pair that has a final unaccented syllable containing the /əl/ or /ən/ sound. Then write the letters that make the final sound in each word you circled.

1. human   moan   _____

2. winner   basin   _____

3. signal   prevail   _____

4. tell   angel   _____

5. nozzle   tale   _____

6. bacon   zone   _____

7. train   captain   _____

8. global   bale   _____

9. barrel   sell   _____

10. real   able   _____

11. listen   lessened   _____

12. practical   all   _____

13. slogan   lagoon   _____

14. will   pencil   _____

15. rain   mountain   _____

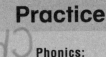

© Macmillan/McGraw-Hill

CA **R 1.0** Word Analysis, Fluency, and Systematic Vocabulary Development

Name _____

| abandon | treacherous | expedition | uninhabited |
| dismantled | labor | triumph | frigid |

A. Write the vocabulary word that best completes each sentence.

1. Glaciers can be _____ because they have deep holes hidden under thin ice.

2. The scientist wanted to go on an _____ to the North Pole to learn more about the animals that live there.

3. Scientists _____ in the freezing weather to build a station.

4. The _____ water was hard for the boat to navigate through because of all the ice and snow.

5. People have been known to _____ over the tough environment at the North Pole.

6. They _____ the tents and packed the pieces onto the boat.

7. The early explorers had to _____ their shacks when they left Antarctica.

8. Until recently, Antarctica was _____ by humans.

B. Read each question. Then write the vocabulary word that best answers the question.

9. If you were on a special mission with a specific purpose, what would you be on? _____

10. What is another word for "be successful" or "win"? _____

11. If a building was not lived in for a very long time, what would it be?

_____

12. How would you describe a road with dangerous curves and no sidewalks?

_____

R 1.0 Word Analysis, Fluency, and Systematic Vocabulary Development

Read each of the following passages from *Spirit of Endurance*. For each passage, tell what problem Shackleton and his crew faced. Explain how they solved the problem.

The crew dismantled the dogloos and brought all the animals back on board because they were afraid that the ice would break under the dogs.

Problem: _____

_____

Solution: _____

_____

Luckily, the destruction of *Endurance* happened in slow motion. This gave the crew plenty of time to unload food and equipment. As the ship continued to break up, the pile of gear on the ice grew larger. Everything that could be taken off the ship was removed. The crew worked without a break. Their survival would depend on saving everything that might come in handy.

Problem: _____

_____

Solution: _____

_____

Their mountaineering equipment wasn't the best gear they could have wished for on a climb such as this one. They had an ax and 50 feet of rope. They studded the soles of their boots with nails for a better grip on the icy peaks. They rested for several days. Then, with food for three days and a small camping stove, they set out, crossing the first snowfield by moonlight.

Problem: _____

_____

Solution: _____

_____

© Macmillan/McGraw-Hill

R 3.2 Identify the main problem or conflict of the plot and explain how it is resolved.

As you read *Spirit of Endurance*, fill in the Problem and Solution Map.

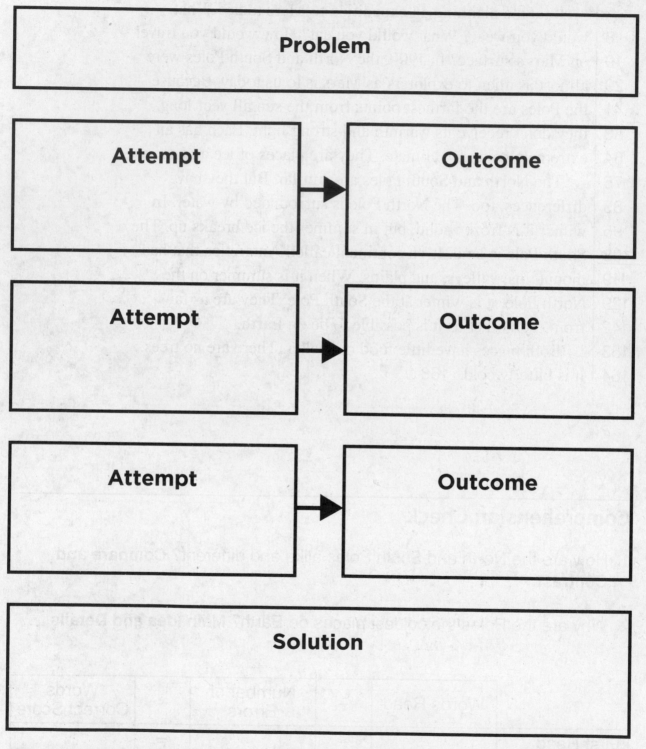

Problem

Attempt

Outcome

Attempt

Outcome

Attempt

Outcome

Solution

How does the information you wrote in the Problem and Solution Map
help you generate questions about *Spirit of Endurance*?

CA **R 3.2** Identify the main problem or conflict of the plot and explain how
it is resolved.

As I read, I will pay attention to pacing.

8	Imagine planning an expedition to Mars today. What would you wear? What would you eat? How would you travel
19	on Mars's surface? In 1900, the North and South Poles were
29	almost as alien to explorers as Mars is to us today. Because
41	the Poles are the farthest points from the sun all year long,
53	they don't receive its warmth and strong light. Each has an
64	extremely cold, dry climate. They are places of ice and snow.
75	The North and South Poles are similar. But they have
85	differences, too. The North Pole is surrounded by water. In
95	winter it is frozen solid, but in summer the ice breaks up. The
108	South Pole is land. It's a continent called Antarctica that has
119	mountains, valleys, and plains. When it is summer on the
129	North Pole, it is winter at the South Pole. They are as far
142	from each other as it is possible to be on Earth.
153	Both places have little food or shelter. There are no trees.
164	It is bitterly cold. 168

Comprehension Check

1. How are the North and South Poles alike and different? **Compare and Contrast**

2. Why are the Poles the coldest places on Earth? **Main Idea and Details**

	Words Read	−	Number of Errors	=	Words Correct Score
First Read		−		=	
Second Read		−		=	

R 1.1 Read aloud narrative and expository text fluently and accurately and with appropriate **pacing**, intonation, and expression.

© Macmillan/McGraw-Hill

A **primary source** is information that comes from the time being studied. **Journals** and **letters** are two types of primary sources. Journals provide daily records written by a person for his or her own use. Letters are a way for people to share information with others through writing.

Use the passage to answer the questions.

October 12

The group and I arrived safely in Antarctica today. The wildlife here is wonderful! I already have seen a colony of Adelie penguins and managed to make some sketches of them in my notebook.

The Adelie penguin

—has a white front and a black back.

—has a white ring around its eyes.

—is about 30 inches tall.

—weighs 11 pounds.

—eats fish. (Must remember to learn more about their diet tomorrow.)

1. What type of primary source is the passage above? How can you tell?

_____

_____

_____

2. In what ways does the primary source show that the author has witnessed the events described?

_____

_____

_____

3. Based on the passage, what is another primary source that you can expect to see with this one?

_____

R 2.1 Understand how text features (e.g., format, graphics, sequence, diagrams, illustrations, charts, maps) make information accessible and usable.

Name _____

A **base word** is a word that can stand alone. A **root word** is a word part that forms the core of a longer word. Base and root words can be changed by adding **affixes**. Affixes are word parts such as **prefixes** that are added to the beginning of a word or **suffixes** that are added to the end of a word. For example, the prefix *un-* means "not." The suffix *-able* means "able to." When these affixes are added to the root word *read*, they form the new word *unreadable*, meaning "not able to be read."

For each word, find the root or base word. Then rewrite the word, dividing it into its parts by drawing slashes. Underline the root or base word.

1. unbreakable ___un/break/able___

2. unkindness ___un/kind/ness___

3. independence ___in/de/pen/dence___

4. leadership ___leader/ship___

5. abandonment ___a/bandon/ment___

6. international ___in/ter/na/tion/al___

7. worthless ___worth/less___

8. autograph ___auto/graph___

9. preview ___pre/view___

10. transportable ___trans/port/able___

© Macmillan/McGraw-Hill

 R 1.0 Word Analysis, Fluency, and Systematic Vocabulary Development

Name _____

- A **pronoun** is a word that takes the place of one or more nouns.
- A singular noun takes a singular pronoun. A plural noun takes a plural pronoun.
- The **antecedent** of a pronoun is the noun (or nouns) to which a pronoun refers.

Complete each sentence by writing the correct pronoun or pronouns.

1. "Hurry up," said Mama Frances, "before _____ change my mind."

2. 'Tricia Ann blew her grandmother a kiss, and then _____ rushed out the door.

3. Mama Frances told 'Tricia Ann, "Those signs can tell _____ where to sit, but _____ can't tell _____ what to think."

4. "_____ am going to Someplace Special," thought 'Tricia Ann as _____ looked out the window.

5. No seats were left in the rear of the bus. _____ had been taken by the crowd of people who got on at the Farmer's Market.

6. Mrs. Grannell and 'Tricia Ann don't like the Jim Crow laws. _____ think the laws are unfair.

7. Jimmy Lee's brother works in Monroe's Restaurant, where _____ is a cook.

8. 'Tricia Ann bought a soda; _____ helped wash down Jimmy Lee's pretzel.

9. When Mr. Willis referred to 'Tricia Ann as an angel, _____ smiled at _____ and said, "No sir. It's just _____."

10. The hotel manager said to 'Tricia Ann, "What makes _____ think that _____ can come inside?"

© Macmillan/McGraw-Hill

Name _____

- A **pronoun** is a word that takes the place of one or more nouns.
- A singular noun takes a singular pronoun. A plural noun takes a plural pronoun.
- The **antecedent** of a pronoun is the noun (or nouns) to which a pronoun refers.

Circle the pronouns that do not agree with their antecedents. Then rewrite the paragraph, using the correct pronouns.

Me like "Goin' Someplace Special" very much. He is a work of historical fiction. They is set during the time when Jim Crow laws were in force. It were harsh laws that treated African Americans unfairly. Them had to sit in the back of buses. Us could not eat at the same restaurants as white people. The same was true for schools, hotels, swimming pools, and even drinking fountains. My grandmother says that he remembers Jim Crow laws. Her says that me wouldn't have liked living in those times. We agree with them.

_____
_____
_____
_____
_____
_____
_____
_____
_____
_____
_____

 LC 1.0 Written and Oral English Language Conventions:

Name _____

1. Read:

When Tia saw Jason's house, she could hardly believe her eyes.
"Your house looks really _____," she said.

2. Consider that Tia might think that Jason's house looks really crowded.
Then she might write: *You have books overflowing from every shelf in
your room. Toys are stacked all over the floor. I have never seen such
a big fish tank. It takes up half the room.*

3. Choose one of the following adjectives to describe the house. Circle it.

old   fancy   crowded

4. Write three new sentences that describe the house so that it matches
the adjective you chose.

_____

_____

_____

_____

_____

_____

_____

_____

_____

_____

_____

_____

A prefix is an affix added to the beginning of a root word. Adding a prefix always changes the meaning of the root word. Look at this list of prefixes and their meanings:

dis- means "not; opposite or lack of"   **re-** means "again"
un- means "not; without"   **mis-** means "wrong, not"

Add one of the prefixes above to each of the words in the sentences below. Use context clues to help you decide which prefix to use.

1. Some people think my sister is _____usual because she wears sandals in the winter.

2. Gilda felt _____couraged about playing soccer after she missed a goal in her last game.

3. Tanya was looking forward to _____uniting with her extended family during her summer vacation.

4. Ben felt _____guided when his coach's advice didn't work out as planned.

5. Jackson _____understood the directions and turned right instead of left.

6. Tilly was _____aware that her little sister had picked up the other phone and was listening to her conversation.

7. I had to _____wrap the present after my baby sister tore the paper off.

8. When we returned to Argentina, we _____discovered the beautiful coastline.

9. "I'm sorry, but we'll be forced to _____connect your phone line if you won't pay the bill," said the representative.

10. "I didn't mean to _____lead you, sir; the elephant statue is not for sale," apologized the woman running the garage sale.

© Macmillan/McGraw-Hill

 R 1.0 Word Analysis, Fluency, and Systematic Vocabulary Development

Name _____

A. Match each vocabulary word with its definition. Write the vocabulary word on the line provided.

mission	function	maze	environment
disasters	gravity	adjusted	zone

1. the air, water, soil, and all the other things surrounding a person, animal, or plant _____

2. special assignment or job _____

3. changed or rearranged _____

4. terrible and unexpected events _____

5. a confusing system of paths or passageways _____

6. to work properly _____

7. the force that attracts objects to Earth _____

8. an area set off from other areas _____

B. Answer each question.

9. Why is **gravity** important? _____

_____

_____

10. How might a **maze** slow you down? _____

_____

_____

Name _____

> The **main idea** of a passage is what the passage is all about. It is the most important point that an author makes about a topic. It is sometimes stated at the beginning of a paragraph. The rest of the sentences then give **details** that help to support or explain the main idea.

Read the two paragraphs below, and identify the main idea of the passage on the lines provided. Then include at least two details that help to support the main idea.

Becoming an Astronaut

Astronauts must go through difficult training because just about everything is done differently in space. Astronauts must learn how to walk and work without gravity. They must practice wearing spacesuits. They must even learn how to eat and sleep while weightless.

Many different machines help the astronauts prepare for space travel. Some machines are simulators, or machines that recreate some of the conditions of outer space here on Earth. The 1/6 Gravity Chair simulates the moon's weaker gravity. On the moon, a person weighs one-sixth of what he or she weighs on Earth. In the Multi-Axis Trainer (MAT), astronauts experience what it is like to be in a tumbling spacecraft. The Five Degrees of Freedom (5DF) Chair simulates the challenges of floating weightlessly.

Main Idea: _____

_____

_____

Details: _____

_____

_____

_____

© Macmillan/McGraw-Hill

CA **R 2.3** Discern main ideas and concepts presented in texts, identifying and assessing evidence that supports those ideas.

Name _____

As you read *Ultimate Field Trip 5*, fill in the Main Idea Chart.

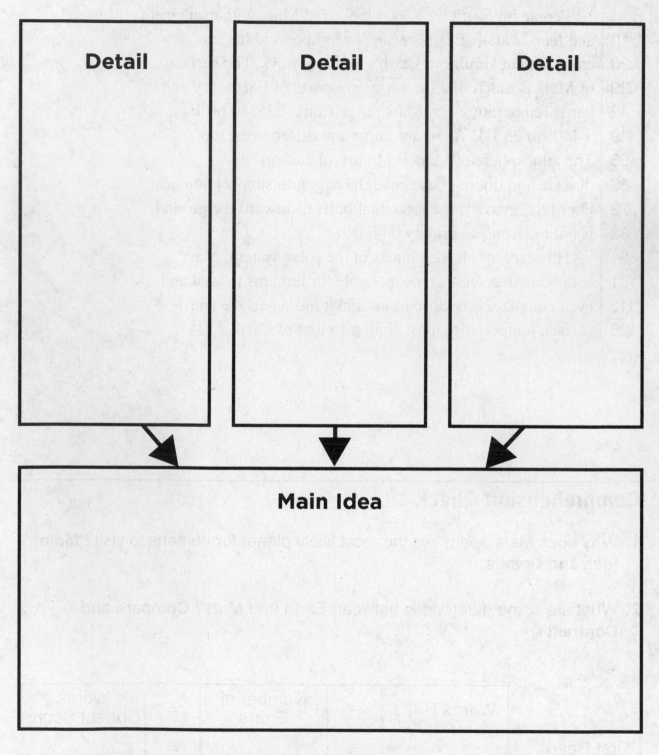

Detail	Detail	Detail

Main Idea

How does the information you wrote in this Main Idea Chart help you generate questions about *Ultimate Field Trip 5*?

R 2.3 Discern main ideas and concepts presented in texts, identifying and assessing evidence that supports those ideas.

Ultimate Field Trip 5: Blasting Off
to Space Academy • **Grade 5/Unit 4**   **207**

As I read, I will pay attention to pronunciation.

	People on Earth have long looked at Mars with excitement
10	and fear. Mars is Earth's nearest neighbor and has an
20	environment similar to Earth's in many ways. The surface
29	of Mars is much like the surface of parts of Earth, dry and
42	hard. Temperatures on Mars range from –225° to 60°F
49	(-140° to 25°C). There are important differences, too.
55	The atmosphere of Mars is almost all carbon
63	dioxide and doesn't have enough oxygen to support humans.
72	On Mars, **gravity**, the force that pulls us toward the ground,
83	is not as strong as gravity on Earth.
91	However, of all the planets in the solar system, Mars
101	is the one that seems most possible for humans to visit and
113	even colonize. It is close to us, and it has a surface and
126	surface temperature most similar to that of Earth. 134

Comprehension Check

1. Why does Mars seem like the most likely planet for humans to visit? **Main Idea and Details**

2. What are some differences between Earth and Mars? **Compare and Contrast**

	Words Read	–	Number of Errors	=	Words Correct Score
First Read		–		=	
Second Read		–		=	

 R 1.1 Read aloud narrative and expository text fluently and accurately and with appropriate pacing, intonation, and expression.

Name _____

Symbolism is the use of a concrete object to represent an abstract idea.

The **moral** is the lesson a story teaches, which can then be used in real life.

Read the following story. Then answer the questions on the lines provided.

One day a huge lion caught a very small mouse in his claws. "Please let me go, and one day I will help you," said the mouse, pleading for his life.

But the lion just laughed. "How could such a small mouse ever help me, the big, strong king of the jungle?" But he let the mouse go, thinking it would be a good joke to eat the tiny fellow the *next* time they met.

The very next day, the big lion stepped out of his lair and right into a hunter's net! He roared with anger and cried in fear. But he could not free himself.

The mouse heard the lion's cry and remembered his promise. He returned to the lion and started nibbling the rope that trapped him. Finally the lion was able to shake himself free.

The lion realized that the mouse had helped him after all. "Dear mouse, I was wrong to tease you for your size. You have saved my life!"

1. What does the mouse symbolize? _____

_____

2. What does the lion symbolize? _____

_____

_____

3. Write the moral of the story in your own words. _____

_____

_____

4. What object in the story symbolizes life's problems? _____

_____

CA R 3.4 Understand that *theme* refers to the meaning or moral of a selection and recognize themes (whether implied or stated directly) in sample works.
R 3.5 Describe the function and effect of common literary devices (e.g., imagery, metaphor, symbolism).

Ultimate Field Trip 5: Blasting Off
to Space Academy • **Grade 5/Unit 4**   **209**

Name _____

If you are reading and come to an unfamiliar word, look at the other words in the sentence. These words might give you hints as to the meaning of the unfamiliar word. We call these hints **context clues**. For example, context clues might **explain** or **describe** an unfamiliar word.

Use context clues to help define the underlined words in the sentences. Circle the letter of the response that best completes each sentence.

1. At the U.S. Space Academy, we felt what it was like to be <u>weightless</u> and float through the air.

   If you are weightless, you are not affected by _____.

   a. air   **b.** gravily   **c.** space

2. Astronauts use <u>simulators</u> in order to feel like what it will be like in space.

   What are simulators? _____

   a. machines   **b.** portals   **c.** missions

3. Since space has no <u>atmosphere</u>, special suits need to be worn to supply astronauts with air and protect them from the sun.

   The special sults provide _____.

   a. sunlight and gravity   **b.** gas and bubbles   **c.** protection from the sun and air

4. The mission crew was asked to <u>deploy</u> the robot that was being stored to work on a broken satellite.

   The robot was deployed to complete an _____.

   a. operation   **b.** orbit   **c.** astronaut

5. Someday it might be possible to <u>colonize</u> the moon so people could live there.

   You cannot colonize a place without _____.

   a. sidewalks   **b.** people   **c.** bikes

CA R 1.0 Word Analysis, Fluency, and Systematic Vocabulary Development

Name _____

Using the Word Study Steps

1. LOOK at the word.

2. SAY the word aloud.

3. STUDY the letters in the word.

4. WRITE the word.

5. CHECK the word.
   Did you spell the word right?
   If not, go back to step 1.

Fill-Ins

Fill in the missing letters of each word to form a spelling word.

1. ___ ___ usual
2. ___ ___ ___ ___ ___ water
3. ___ ___ gain
4. ___ ___ ___ merge
5. ___ ___ aware
6. ___ ___ ___ connect
7. ___ ___ plenish
8. ___ ___ important
9. ___ ___ ___ specific
10. ___ ___ ___ honest

11. ___ ___ unite
12. ___ ___ discover
13. ___ ___ wrap
14. ___ ___ friendly
15. ___ ___ ___ courage
16. ___ ___ finished
17. ___ ___ ___ guide
18. ___ ___ freeze
19. ___ ___ ___ ___ whelm
20. ___ ___ paired

LC 1.5 Spell roots, suffixes, prefixes, contractions, and syllable constructions correctly.

Name _____

A. Circle the misspelled words in the passage. Write the words correctly on the lines below.

I know it is unusuall to love water as much I do. People tell me all the time that they were unawaire I was such a water nut. Sometimes they are even unfreindly about it, telling me I should get my head back on land. I think this is unimportint, because there is so much going on at the underrwater level. Why sit on dry ground when I could submerdge my body and mind and explore this exciting universe?

1. _____   3. _____   5. _____

2. _____   4. _____   6. _____

B. Writing Activity

Continue writing the story. Use at least four more spelling words.

_____

_____

_____

_____

_____

_____

_____

_____

_____

 LC 1.5 Spell roots, suffixes, prefixes, contractions, and syllable constructions correctly.

Name _____

> • Use a **subject pronoun** as the subject of a sentence.
> • Use an **object pronoun** after an action verb or after a word such as *for, at, of, with,* or *to.*

Correct each sentence by writing the correct pronoun on the line. Then write whether the pronoun is a subject or object pronoun.

1. As Carlos and Gloria walked down the road, them saw Dos Dedos.
   _____

2. "Me will catch Dos Dedos," Carlos said. _____

3. Carlos's clothes smelled terrible; in fact, the smell of they was unbearable.
   _____

4. When his mother came into the kitchen, her noticed the smell.
   _____

5. Carlos did not want to talk about the smell, so him slipped out the back door. _____

6. Carlos picked tomatoes from the garden and squeezed they into the bathtub. _____

7. Him scrubbed with a cloth soaked in tomato juice. _____

8. The next day, Carlos went to church; him sat near the back.
   _____

9. Carlos was embarrassed by the smell of his shoes; everyone in church could smell they. _____

10. At dinner, his parents said, "Us think Carlos is unusually quiet."
    _____

Name _____

- **Subject pronouns** are the subjects in a sentence.
- **Object pronouns** receive the action of a verb or follow a preposition.

Circle all of the incorrect subject and object pronouns. Then rewrite the passage.

Carlos and Gloria were good friends. Them often played together after them finished their chores and homework. When Carlos and Gloria were together, they noticed Dos Dedos, a skunk them had named. Carlos wanted to show off for Gloria, so him tried to catch the skunk by the tail. The skunk sprayed he, and Carlos was embarrassed. The smell remained on Carlos's shoes. When him wore they to church the next day, everyone noticed the awful smell. Carlos's father took he shopping for a new pair of shoes.

_____

_____

_____

_____

_____

_____

_____

_____

_____

_____

 CA **LC 1.0** Written and Oral English Language Conventions

© Macmillan/McGraw-Hill

Name _____

1. Read:

   It's not very bright in here and not very warm either. Once in a while I hear a penguin honking, but mostly it's the chatter of other kids I hear. I press my hands against the cool glass and watch a giant sea turtle float by.

2. Name the setting for those sentences _____

3. List three details that showed you that setting _____,
   _____, _____

4. Choose one of the places listed below. Consider choosing a place that you know well so you can think of lots of details to describe it. Circle your choice.

   Computer lab   school   field trip to zoo   grocery store   swimming pool   bus

   movie theatre   arcade   fast food restaurant   mall   amusement park   library

5. Now, imagine that you are in that setting that you chose. Write 5-7 sentences describing your setting without telling what the setting is.

   _____

   _____

   _____

   _____

   _____

   _____

   _____

   _____

   _____

   _____

   _____

Homographs are words that are spelled the same but have different meanings. Sometimes words that are homographs will be accented, or stressed, on different syllables. The part of speech and the meaning of the word depend on which syllable is accented.

Circle the syllable in each underlined homograph that should be accented to make the sentence correct. Use a dictionary to help you.

1. An election is a <u>contest</u> between two or more candidates.

2. The lawyer will <u>contest</u> the decision the judge made.

3. Candidates must watch their <u>conduct</u> while debating each other.

4. The maestro will <u>conduct</u> the orchestra.

5. The <u>conflict</u> was broadcast on television.

6. Luckily, her schedule did not <u>conflict</u> with ours.

7. Politics is a <u>subject</u> that many people feel strongly about.

8. The king did not <u>subject</u> his people to cruel punishments.

9. Every <u>minute</u> detail must be followed in the line of presidential succession.

10. A <u>minute</u> passed before I was called into the doctor's office.

11. He will probably <u>refuse</u> to run in the election.

12. Tim does not throw <u>refuse</u> in the recycling bin.

13. I am <u>content</u> to live in a democracy that offers so many freedoms.

14. The <u>content</u> of her speech was in the outline.

© Macmillan/McGraw-Hill

 R 1.0 Word Analysis, Fluency, and Systematic Vocabulary Development

Name _____

A. Write a sentence to answer each question. Make sure your sentence shows that you understand the meaning of the vocabulary word in the question.

1. What **supplies** might people need during the storm? _____

_____

_____

2. What is the most **violent** weather you have ever seen? _____

_____

_____

3. How can you get **involved** to help people after a bad storm? _____

_____

_____

4. What might be the **impact** if a tree fell on a house? _____

_____

_____

5. Which plants **survived** the storm? _____

_____

_____

B. Now write a sentence using one of the vocabulary words.

6. _____

_____

_____

_____

_____

_____

_____

Name _____

A **fact** is a statement that can be checked and proven true, such as *Marta is eleven years old*. An **opinion** is a statement of someone's beliefs or feelings and cannot be proven true, such as *Marta is the nicest girl in our class*. Some sentences include both facts and opinions.

A. Read the paragraph below. Underline the statements of fact. Circle the statements of opinion.

Last year, more than 15,000 people climbed Mount Shasta. At 14,162 feet, Mount Shasta is the tallest mountain in California. It is also the most beautiful.

Some of the climbers who reach the top of Mount Shasta have never climbed a mountain before. Others have climbed for many years. Seventeen different routes lead to the top of Mount Shasta. Mountain climbing is exciting and it is also very dangerous. People who climb with others have fewer accidents than people who climb alone.

B. Statements of fact can be checked and proven true. Write one statement of fact from the passage above. Then tell how you might check the statement of fact.

Fact: _____

Check: _____

 R 2.5 Distinguish facts, supported inferences, and opinions in text.

© Macmillan/McGraw-Hill

Name _____

As you read *Heroes in Time of Need*, fill in the Fact and Opinion Chart.

Fact	Opinion

How does the information you wrote in the Fact and Opinion Chart help you evaluate *Heroes in Time of Need*?

CA R 2.5 Distinguish facts, supported inferences, and opinions in text.

Heroes in Time of Need
Grade 5/Unit 4   219

Name _____

As I read, I will pay attention to phrasing.

8	The Mojave and Colorado deserts are two entirely different ecosystems that exist side by side. Although they
17	are both arid, they look different, have different weather, and
27	are occupied by different living things.
33	These deserts are different because they are at two
42	different elevations, their height above sea level. The
50	Colorado Desert is below 3,000 feet in elevation. It has less
60	rainfall, fewer plants, and higher temperatures than the
68	Mojave Desert. The Mojave is over 3,000 feet in elevation.
77	It has more rainfall, and temperatures can dip below freezing.
87	So, Joshua Tree National Park contains two quite different
96	deserts. But the most remarkable thing about this park is
106	the area between the two deserts. This transition area is very
117	narrow, generally less than a mile wide. In this slim zone,
128	animals and plants from both sides of the park are abundant.
139	But the cholla (CHOY-uh) cactus rules the zone. Don't walk
148	too close to this "jumping" cactus or the spiny needles will
159	snag you. Ouch! 162

Comprehension Check

1. Compare and contrast the Mojave and Colorado deserts. **Compare and Contrast**

2. What is the transition area? **Relevant Facts**

	Words Read	–	Number of Errors	=	Words Correct Score
First Read		–		=	
Second Read		–		=	

© Macmillan/McGraw-Hill

 R 1.1 Read aloud narrative and expository text fluently and accurately and with appropriate pacing, intonation, and expression.

Name _____

If you can identify the **parts of a book**, you can easily find the information that you need.

Read the chart below. Then write the correct part of a book to answer each question.

Front of a book	Back of a book
Title page: tells the book's title and author	**Index:** an alphabetical listing of names and topics and the page numbers that apply to each item
Chapter titles: tell the names of the chapters	**Glossary:** an alphabetical list of words and definitions
Table of contents: lists the chapter titles and the page number on which each chapter begins	**Endnotes:** notes that give additional information
	Bibliography: a list of writings that includes the date and place of publication

1. Where will you find notes that give additional information? _____

2. Where can you find the definitions of words? _____

3. Where are the book chapters listed? _____

4. Which two parts of a book are arranged in alphabetical order? _____
_____

5. How could you learn whether a topic or person you are researching is

   mentioned in a book? _____

6. How could you find information about books or articles that an author used

   to write the book you are reading? _____

W 1.3 Use organizational features of printed text (e.g., citations, endnotes, bibliographic references) to locate relevant information.

Cause/Effect Writing Frame

A. Summarize *Heroes in Time of Need*. **Use the Cause/Effect Writing Frame below.**

In 2004 and 2005, there were devastating hurricanes, tsunamis, and earthquakes around the world.

As a result of these disasters, _____

_____

_____ .

This **caused** students in Texas to help out by _____

_____

_____ .

This **caused** students in California to help out by _____

_____

_____ .

This **caused** students in Maryland to help out by _____

_____

_____ .

These disasters brought out the best in people all over the world.

B. Rewrite the completed summary on another sheet of paper. Keep it as a model for writing a summary of an article or selection using this text structure.

 R 2.0 Reading Comprehension

Name _____

Some English words originally come from Greek or Latin words. Knowing the meaning of **Greek and Latin word roots** can help you figure out the meaning of unfamiliar words.

Greek Root	Meaning	Latin Root	Meaning
bio	life	aqua	water
pod	foot	port	carry
graph	write	man	hand

Circle the letter next to the correct meaning of each word. Use information from the chart to help you.

1. manual
a. done by a man, not a woman
b. done by hand

2. biopsy
a. a test for two eyes
b. a test of material from a living body

3. graphite
a. a mineral used for writing
b. a mineral that floats in water

4. aquatic
a. growing or living in water
b. moving quickly

5. podiatrist
a. a person who studies plants
b. a foot doctor

6. transport
a. to carry from one place to another
b. to play a game in different places

CA R 1.4 Know abstract, derived roots and affixes from Greek and Latin and use this knowledge to analyze the meaning of complex words (e.g., *controversial*).

Name _____

Using the Word Study Steps

1. LOOK at the word.
2. SAY the word aloud.
3. STUDY the letters in the word.
4. WRITE the word.
5. CHECK the word.
   Did you spell the word right?
   If not, go back to step 1.

A. Find and Circle

Find and circle each of the spelling words in this puzzle. Words may read forward, backward, upward, downward, or diagonally.

```
C E S U F E R F T T T E M T K E T T E T Y H
O C O M B A T G N S C M F G E R C N C C C S
N M I N U T E D E E U H I K E I T A O R I U
T Y P G N Q A N T T D G V S L R R M A J C B
R T S E T N O C N O N B E F A T P E X X H J
A T R E S N I F O R O D N N X A S V K I W E
C P R E S E N T C P C O C E C E L E B E R C
T P E R M I T S W N C E L T R E X C U S E T
```

B. List the words below as you find them in the puzzle.

1. _____   6. _____   11. _____   16. _____

2. _____   7. _____   12. _____   17. _____

3. _____   8. _____   13. _____   18. _____

4. _____   9. _____   14. _____   19. _____

5. _____   10. _____   15. _____   20. _____

 LC 1.5 Spell roots, suffixes, prefixes, contractions, and syllable constructions correctly.

Name _____

A. Circle the misspelled words in the passage. Write the words correctly on the lines below.

A small crowd gathered outside the White House to hear the President speak. The subjeckt of his speech was voting. A team of experts had done resurch about how many people actually voted. "There is no eksuse for not voting," he began. "The Constitution purmits each of you to take part in the election process. I intend to conduckt a survey asking people why they chose not to vote. When I have that information, I will preesent it to you so that we may work on solving this problem."

1. _____ 3. _____ 5. _____

2. _____ 4. _____ 6. _____

B. Writing Activity

Write a paragraph about what you could do to encourage more people to vote in presidential elections. Use four words from your spelling list.

_____
_____
_____
_____
_____
_____
_____
_____
_____
_____
_____

LC 1.5 Spell roots, suffixes, prefixes, contractions, and syllable constructions correctly.

Heroes in Time of Need
Grade 5/Unit 4   **225**

Name _____

- The verbs *have* and *be* take special forms in the present tense. Make sure to use the form that agrees with the subject of the sentence.

Rewrite each sentence. Correct all errors in pronoun-verb agreement.

1. Our country has two major political parties; they is the Democratic party and the Republican party.

_____

_____

2. They has animals that represent each party.

_____

3. The Democrats have their animal; it are a donkey.

_____

4. The Republicans have theirs, too; it am an elephant.

_____

5. The donkey is associated with Andrew Jackson; it be a symbol of strong will.

_____

_____

6. Cartoonist Thomas Nast made the symbols famous; they is in his cartoons.

_____

_____

7. Republicans like the elephant, and they has no problem with it.

_____

_____

8. Democrats like their donkey because it are smart and brave.

_____

_____

 LC 1.0 Written and Oral English Language Conventions

Name _____

- The verbs *have* and *be* take special forms in the present tense.
  Use the form that agrees with the subject of the sentence.

Rewrite the passage, using the correct forms of *have* and *be*.

Russia are located in both Europe and Asia. It have mountains, plains, and large forests. Also, it be rich in natural resources such as gold and coal. Since 1991, Russia have been an independent nation. The president of Russia be elected by the Russian people. The government in Russia be considered a democracy.

Before 1991, Russia belonged to a group of countries called the Union of Soviet Socialist Republics, or U.S.S.R. The U.S.S.R. had a form of government called communism. In communist countries, the government have control of most property and businesses.

_____

_____

_____

_____

_____

_____

_____

_____

_____

_____

_____

_____

Name _____

Writing Rubric

	4 Excellent	3 Good	2 Fair	1 Unsatisfactory
	Ideas and Content/ Genre	Ideas and Content/ Genre	Ideas and Content/ Genre	Ideas and Content/ Genre
	Organization and Focus	Organization and Focus	Organization and Focus	Organization and Focus
	Sentence Structure/ Fluency	Sentence Structure/ Fluency	Sentence Structure/ Fluency	Sentence Structure/ Fluency
	Conventions	Conventions	Conventions	Conventions
	Word Choice	Word Choice	Word Choice	Word Choice
	Voice	Voice	Voice	Voice
	Presentation	Presentation	Presentation	Presentation

© Macmillan/McGraw-Hill

CA W 1.0 Writing Strategies

The sounds you hear in the final syllable of the words *culture* and *measure* can be spelled in different ways, including **-ture** and **-sure**. Listen to the final syllables in the words measure (**/zhər/** sound) and culture (**/chər/** sound).

A. Choose the word in each pair that has a final syllable that sounds like /zhər/, as in *measure*. Then write the word on the line.

1. vulture / closure _____

2. pleasure / rancher _____

3. fissure / fracture _____

4. mixture / treasure _____

5. enclosure / picture _____

6. leisure / fixture _____

B. Choose the word in each pair that has a final syllable that sounds like /chər/, as in *culture*. Then write the word on the line.

7. legislature / leisure _____

8. future / composure _____

9. fixture / pleasure _____

10. assure / nature _____

11. mixture / erasure _____

12. pasture / ledger _____

13. creature / enclosure _____

14. pressure / gesture _____

15. exposure / nurture _____

CA **R 1.0** Word Analysis, Fluency, and Systematic Vocabulary Development

A. Label each sentence *True* if the boldface vocabulary word is used correctly. If a sentence is *False*, explain why on the line below.

1. A **defective** toy is in good working order. _____

   _____

2. If positions are **reversed** during a class debate, your team begins arguing

   for the opposite opinion. _____

   _____

3. A **meteor** comes from deep inside Earth. _____

   _____

4. A **robot** is a living thing. _____

   _____

5. If you see a tree branch that is **dangling**, it is lying on the ground. _____

   _____

6. My sister played with a spinning top that **rotated** in circles. _____

   _____

7. The tired runner **staggered** to the finish line, looking as if he might fall down.

   _____

8. You might use the **tokens** from a board game to buy lunch. _____

   _____

B. Write two sentences that each includes one vocabulary word.

9. _____

   _____

10. _____

   _____

CA **R 1.0** Word Analysis, Fluency, and Systematic Vocabulary Development

Name _____

As you read, you can **draw conclusions** by thinking about information the author provides and what you know from your own experience. This helps you analyze and better understand a story.

Read the two paragraphs below, then answer the questions. Describe the clues that helped you draw a conclusion.

It was almost noon. Maria had been watching the clock for the last half hour. Wouldn't Mrs. Jones ever stop talking? Maria thought again of the green apple in her lunchbox. She could almost taste it. Then her stomach began to growl.

What conclusion can you draw about Maria? _____

_____

Story clues: _____

_____

Experience clues: _____

_____

Evan picked at his cereal. He knew he should have studied harder last night, but the dates all ran together in his head. Why did he have to learn American history anyway? For the third time, his mother told him to hurry. He put on his coat. He felt a sudden wave of dread.

What conclusion can you draw about Evan? _____

_____

Story clues: _____

_____

Experience clues: _____

_____

R 2.4 Draw inferences, conclusions, or generalizations about text and support them with textual evidence and prior knowledge.

Zathura • **Grade 5/Unit 4**   **231**

© Macmillan/McGraw-Hill

Name _____

As you read *Zathura*, fill in the Conclusions Diagrams.

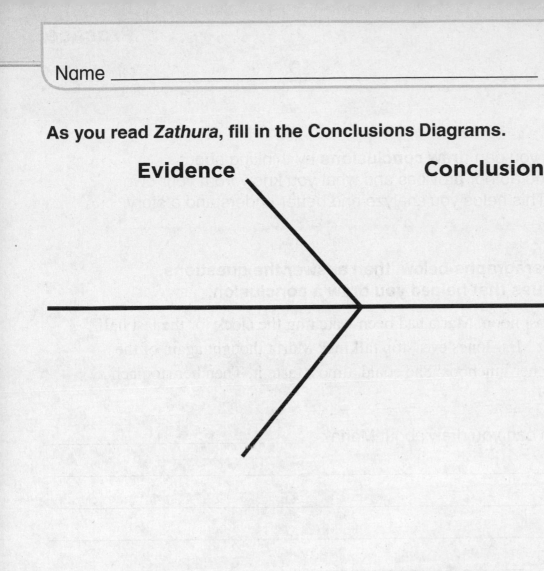

Evidence

Conclusion

Evidence

Conclusion

How does the information you wrote in the Conclusions Diagrams help
you make inferences and analyze *Zathura*?

R 2.4 Draw inferences, **conclusions**, or generalizations about text and
support them with textual evidence and prior knowledge.

Name _____

As I read, I will pay attention to intonation and phrasing.

	Robomation was Gregory and Anthony's favorite
6	magazine. It had articles about space exploration, science
14	experiments kids could do at home, and stories about
23	traveling to other planets. Plus, winners of the contests got
33	out-of-this-world prizes. Or so Gregory heard. He had yet to
43	win a single contest despite many, many tries.
51	"Gregory! Anthony!" That was Gregory's mom calling
58	them from the kitchen. From her tone, Gregory could tell
68	there was something she wanted him to do, and he dreaded it.
80	"Yes, Mom," he answered right away. "What is it?"
89	"Why don't you go outside?" she called out. "It's such a
100	beautiful day. Go get some fresh air and exercise. A bunch of
112	kids are shooting baskets across the street."
119	Gregory knew his mother was talking about Jordan Veras
128	and the "cool" gang. Gregory didn't fit in with their group,
139	though he had tried often. Maybe, if he were someone else. . . .
150	"Okay, Mom," Gregory sighed. He knew his mom was
159	right about the exercise. 163

Comprehension Check

1. Why was *Robomation* Gregory and Anthony's favorite magazine? **Main Idea and Details**

2. Why isn't Gregory excited about going outside? **Plot Development**

	Words Read	–	Number of Errors	=	Words Correct Score
First Read		–		=	
Second Read		–		=	

R 1.1 Read aloud narrative and expository text fluently and accurately
and with appropriate pacing, **intonation**, and expression.

Name _____

A **toolbar** is a strip of symbols that allows you to visit different features on a Web site. A **link** is an electronic connection on a Web site that provides direct access to other information.

Use the Web site page to answer the questions.

www.space_skyview.com

Home   Browse   Search   Astronomers

A Better View of SPACE

Links related to this topic

Related Articles

▶ Famous Astronomers

▶ Modern Astronomers

▶ Telescopes

For thousands of years, people have observed objects in the night sky. The earliest astronomers relied on what they could see with their eyes. They watched the stars and planets and charted their positions. Then, in 1609, an Italian scientist named Galileo Galilei developed a better method of studying the planets. Galileo started using a **telescope**, a device that makes distant objects appear closer.

Galileo did not invent the telescope, but he did develop a version of this device that was more powerful than any that had come before. Galileo was the first to see craters on the moon. He soon found out that Earth was not the only planet with a moon—other planets, including Jupiter, had moons too. Galileo's discoveries made modern astronomy possible.

1. What buttons can you find on the toolbar? _____

_____

2. How can links help you get information? _____

_____

3. On this Web site, how would you get information about Galileo's life?

_____

4. What feature would you select to learn about current astronomers?

_____

CA R 2.1 Understand how text features (e.g., format, graphics, sequence, diagrams, illustrations, charts, maps) make information accessible and usable.

Name _____

An **analogy** is a comparison of two pairs of words. **Synonyms**, or words with the same meaning, can be used in analogies. The two words in the first pair match in the same way that the two words in the second pair match.

Read this example: Big is to large as thin is to _____slim_____.

The words **big** and **large** are synonyms, and the words **thin** and **slim** are synonyms.

Complete each analogy by writing a synonym for the first word in the second pair of words.

1. Take is to grab as break is to _____.

2. Freedom is to liberty as talk is to _____.

3. Find is to discover as work is to _____.

4. Try is to attempt as shiver is to _____.

5. Car is to automobile as column is to _____.

6. Location is to place as choose is to _____.

7. Gift is to present as hole is to _____.

8. Country is to nation as ruler is to _____.

9. Drum is to instrument as friend is to _____.

10. Meal is to dinner as land is to _____.

Name _____

Using the Word Study Steps

1. LOOK at the word.
2. SAY the word aloud.
3. STUDY the letters in the word.
4. WRITE the word.
5. CHECK the word.
   Did you spell the word right?
   If not, go back to step 1.

A. Fill-Ins

Fill in the missing letters of each word to form a spelling word.

1. fu ___ ___ ___ e
2. crea ___ ___ ___ e
3. sear ___ ___ ___ ___
4. fea ___ ___ ___ e
5. frac ___ ___ ___ e
6. ges ___ ___ ___ e
7. legisla ___ ___ ___ e
8. pres ___ ___ ___ e
9. mea ___ ___ ___ e
10. mix ___ ___ ___ e

11. mois ___ ___ ___ e
12. na ___ ___ ___ e
13. pas ___ ___ ___ e
14. plea ___ ___ ___ e
15. a ___ ___ ___ e
16. stret ___ ___ e ___
17. trea ___ ___ ___ e
18. ran ___ ___ e ___
19. but ___ ___ e ___
20. lec ___ ___ ___ e

B. Write the Words

Use the lines below to practice writing the spelling words.

1. _____
2. _____
3. _____
4. _____
5. _____
6. _____
7. _____
8. _____
9. _____
10. _____
11. _____
12. _____
13. _____
14. _____
15. _____
16. _____
17. _____
18. _____
19. _____
20. _____

LC 1.5 Spell roots, suffixes, prefixes, contractions, and syllable constructions correctly.

© Macmillan/McGraw-Hill

Name _____

A. Circle the misspelled words in the passage. Write the words correctly on the lines below.

Andrew walked outside. He felt as if something were different. There wasn't a creechur in sight. There was more moysture in the air. The sky had changed from a beautiful asure to a dark gray. Soon there would be a mixchure of rain, wind, and flooding. Natchure was about to demonstrate the effects of a natural disaster. Andrew put a cup on the porch to meazure the rainfall and headed inside to watch.

1. _____   3. _____   5. _____

2. _____   4. _____   6. _____

B. Writing Activity

Write a paragraph about what you would do if you found out that a hurricane was going to hit your town. Use four words from your spelling list.

_____

_____

_____

_____

_____

_____

_____

_____

_____

_____

_____

LC 1.5 Spell roots, suffixes, prefixes, contractions, and syllable constructions correctly.

Zathura • Grade 5/Unit 4   **237**

Name _____

> • Some **possessive pronouns** are used before nouns (*my, your, his, her, its, our, your, their*).
> • Some **possessive pronouns** stand alone in a sentence and function as nouns (*mine, yours, his, hers, its, ours, yours, theirs*).

Read each sentence. Find the incorrect possessive pronoun and write it correctly on the line.

1. What kinds of storms do you have in yours town? _____

2. In my, there are hurricanes. _____

3. Mine home is located near the coast of North Carolina. _____

4. Hurricane Fran caused a lot of damage to ours house. _____

5. During the last hurricane, my sister was frightened when strong winds

   broke a window in hers room. _____

6. Many large trees fell in Phil and Gina's yard and ruined theirs shed.

   _____

7. Three big trees fell on top of the shed, crashing through her roof.

   _____

8. However, the roof on ours house was not damaged. _____

9. We have learned about hurricanes in mine science class.

   _____

10. The people in ours neighborhood help one another when hurricanes

    hit. _____

 LC 1.0 Written and Oral English Language Conventions

Name _____

- A **possessive pronoun** can take the place of a possessive noun. It shows who or what has or owns something.
- Some possessive pronouns are used before nouns. Some possessive pronouns stand alone in a sentence and function as nouns.

Read the following passage. Circle all of the incorrect possessive pronouns. Then rewrite the passage.

   In mine hometown, the most dangerous storms are tornadoes. In fact, a town near my was destroyed twice by tornadoes. Ours cousins live in that town. Many people lost possessions, and some lost theirs homes. Ours cousins' home wasn't destroyed, although theirs yard was in bad shape. My cousin said that hers house is more vulnerable to tornadoes than hers neighbor's house because hers house is more exposed than his'. It sits on top of a hill, and its' big windows face toward the southwest. I'm glad ours house is in a well-protected area and that we have several battery-powered radios for emergencies.

_____

_____

_____

_____

_____

_____

_____

_____

_____

_____

1. Read the sentence: *Cory trudged through the swamp.*

2. Consider what you learn from this sentence. You know Cory is walking in a swamp. It seems like it is a muddy swamp because he trudged through it.

3. Consider how Cory feels. Is he worried? Is he happy? Is he lost? Maybe he is upset about his sneakers. Cory nearly cried at the thought that his brand-new sneakers would end up brown and stinky. He hated that the bottoms of his jeans were getting muddy.

4. Write 3 sentences that describe Cory "trudging" through the swamp. Include details that let the reader know what Cory is like as a character.

_____

_____

_____

_____

_____

_____

_____

_____

_____

_____

_____

_____

_____

_____

_____

© Macmillan/McGraw-Hill

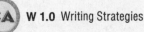 **W 1.0** Writing Strategies

The suffixes **-ance** and **-ence** mean "the state or quality of." They are suffixes with unstressed vowels.

Complete each word by adding *-ance* or *-ence*. Then write the completed word on the line. Use a dictionary to help you find the syllable that is stressed. Say each new word to hear how it is pronounced. Circle the stressed syllable in each word.

1. ambul_____ _____

2. resid_____ _____

3. bal_____ _____

4. subst_____ _____

5. import_____ _____

6. assist_____ _____

7. abs_____ _____

8. persist_____ _____

9. attend_____ _____

10. disturb_____ _____

11. independ_____ _____

12. perform_____ _____

13. refer_____ _____

14. eleg_____ _____

15. emerg_____ _____

Name _____

A. Match the vocabulary word with its definition. Then write the letter of the correct word on the line.

1. ease _____

2. scenery _____

3. bundle _____

4. fused _____

5. guaranteed _____

6. supervise _____

7. frustrated _____

8. coordination _____

a. joined together

b. disappointed or kept from doing something

c. working well together

d. move carefully or slowly

e. landscape

f. group of things held together

g. assured

h. watch and direct

B. Fill in the paragraph using the eight vocabulary words from section A.

My uncle _____ that we would enjoy the

_____ of the mountains and lake. But the trip did not start out

great. We tried to _____ the tent out of the stuffed car, but it

wouldn't budge. Next, my older brother became _____ when

he noticed the _____ of hamburgers was _____

together. Unfortunately, we did not bring any other food for dinner. We relied

on the _____ of all three of us to get the hamburgers

separated. While my uncle cooked, he wanted to _____ me as

I unpacked the rest of the car. I was about to ask to go home when I saw two

baby deer playing with each other. I guess being in nature is worth a frozen

dinner and overstuffed car.

© Macmillan/McGraw-Hill

 R 1.0 Word Analysis, Fluency, and Systematic Vocabulary Development

Name _____

When you read a story, you **make judgments** about the
characters and the things they say or do. Making judgments
helps you evaluate what you read and understand the **plot
development** of a story.

Answer each question below. Then explain your answers.

1. It takes Uncle Curtis three tries to find the exit to Mount Tamalpais.
When Uncle Curtis finally makes it to the park, he is given a map of the
campgrounds. He "didn't even glance at it but threw it into the backseat." Do
you think he made a wise decision when he chose to ignore the map?

_____

_____

_____

2. Teddy and Bobby wear clothes appropriate for a San Francisco summer—
sweatshirts and corduroys. The weather forecast for Mount Tamalpais
is hot and humid. Teddy and Bobby decide to pack only sweatshirts and
corduroys to take to the camp. What do you think of their clothing decision?

_____

_____

_____

3. Teddy and Bobby find that the hot dogs and hamburgers, which Teddy had
packed in dry ice, are frozen solid. But Uncle Curtis tries to grill the frozen
food before it has thawed. Do you think that Teddy's method of packing the
meat was successful?

_____

_____

_____

As you read *Skunk Scout*, fill in the Judgments Chart.

Action		Judgment
	→	
	→	
	→	
	→	

How does the information you wrote in this Judgments Chart help you
monitor comprehension of *Skunk Scout*?

 R 2.0 Reading Comprehension (Focus on Informational Materials)

As I read, I will pay attention to expression.

9	Can you guess what main force created the Grand Canyon? It was the mighty Colorado River.
16	The Colorado is a huge, powerful river. In the spring,
26	melted snow fills the river, and it becomes swift and wild.
37	The river picks up rocks, huge boulders, sand, and pebbles
47	and carries them along. Over millions of years, this gritty
57	river water carved into layer after layer of rock. It carved the
69	deepest canyon of all, the Grand Canyon.
76	One reason the river could carve the rock is that the rock
88	was soft. Soft for rock, that is! Back in time, before there was
101	a Grand Canyon, oceans covered the land.
108	Over millions of years, broken seashells, sand, mud, and
117	clay fell to the bottom of the sea. These small bits of matter
130	that settle on the sea bottom are called sediment. Over
140	millions of years, the sediment turned into rock, called
149	sedimentary rock. And this rock was soft enough for the river
160	to be able to carve a deeper and deeper path through it.
172	But the Colorado River was not the only force to form the
184	Grand Canyon. 186

Comprehension Check

1. How did the Colorado River help form the Grand Canyon? **Main Idea and Details**

2. What is sedimentary rock? **Relevant Facts and Details**

	Words Read	–	Number of Errors	=	Words Correct Score
First Read		–		=	
Second Read		–		=	

R 1.1 Read aloud narrative and expository text fluently and accurately and with appropriate pacing, intonation, and **expression**.

An **interview** is a conversation in which one person asks another person questions and records the answers.

Read the following interview. Then answer the questions that follow.

Reporter:	Can you please state your full name and occupation?
Maria Chavez:	Maria Chavez, fifth-grade teacher.
Reporter:	Ms. Chavez, how is it that you became a teacher?
Chavez:	I have always loved kids. As a young girl growing up in Mexico, I always took care of the children in the neighborhood. I loved to babysit for my cousins, and I enjoyed helping them with their schoolwork. I liked helping them learn! So, when I graduated from college, I thought teaching would be the best way to make a living and do what I am good at. I chose fifth grade because I think this is the most exciting year of elementary school.
Reporter:	Do you have a favorite subject to teach?
Chavez:	I like them all. I enjoy teaching English because we get to read so many wonderful stories, but when it's time to start math or science, I roll up my sleeves for that, too! I just think it's all so exciting.

1. Who is the reporter interviewing?

_____

2. Who is this person?

_____

_____

3. What led her to her current profession?

_____

_____

4. Where did Ms. Chavez grow up?

_____

R 2.1 Understand how text features (e.g., format, graphics, sequence, diagrams, illustrations, charts, maps) make information accessible and usable.

© Macmillan/McGraw-Hill

Name _____

Words with more than one meaning are **multiple-meaning words**. You can use **context clues**, or other words in the sentence, to help you figure out the meaning. Sometimes you must use a **dictionary** to learn the different meanings of the word.

A. Read each sentence. Then circle the letter next to the correct meaning of each underlined word.

1. My first camping trip <u>might</u> have been a disaster, but it turned out great.

   a. physical strength   **b.** expressing possibility or doubt

2. We had to change a flat tire on the way to the campground, but the <u>spare</u> tire worked fine.

   a. extra   **b.** hold back or avoid

3. After that, we set up our tent near some trees and <u>brush</u>.

   a. object with bristles on a handle   **b.** heavy growth of bushes

4. <u>Cavities</u> in the rocks near the river were the perfect place to store our towels while we swam in the lake.

   a. hollow places   **b.** decayed spots on teeth

5. He still had some <u>change</u> in his pocket.

   a. to become different   **b.** coins

6. As the day came to a <u>close</u>, I was happy to be camping.

   a. end   **b.** shut

B. Use a dictionary to find two meanings of each multiple-meaning word listed below.

7. jam   **a.** _____

           b. _____

8. coat   **a.** _____

           b. _____

Name _____

Using the Word Study Steps

1. LOOK at the word.

2. SAY the word aloud.

3. STUDY the letters in the word.

4. WRITE the word.

5. CHECK the word.
   Did you spell the word right?
   If not, go back to step 1.

A. Fill-Ins

Fill in the missing letters of each word to form a spelling word.

1. ignor ___ ___ ___ e

2. abs ___ ___ ___ e

3. persist ___ ___ ___ e

4. appea ___ ___ ___ ce

5. reluc ___ ___ ___ ce

6. resid ___ ___ ___ e

7. distur ___ ___ ___ ce

8. brill ___ ___ ___ ce

9. ambu ___ ___ ___ ce

10. resis ___ ___ ___ ce

11. dista ___ ___ ___

12. assis ___ a ___ ___ e

13. ba ___ a ___ ___ e

14. rad ___ ___ n ___ e

15. impor ___ ___ n ___ e

16. hesit ___ ___ ___ e

17. depen ___ ___ ___ ce

18. subs ___ ___ n ___ e

19. atten ___ ___ ___ ce

20. perfor ___ ___ n ___ e

B. Use the spelling words above to help you write a poem of at least four lines.

21. _____

22. _____

23. _____

24. _____

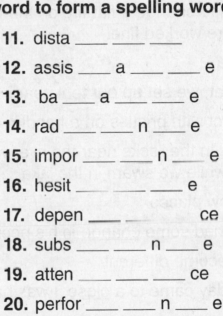

© Macmillan/McGraw-Hill

LC 1.5 Spell roots, suffixes, prefixes, contractions, and syllable constructions correctly.

Name _____

A. Circle the misspelled words in the passage. Write the words correctly on the lines below.

The Basketmaker ran a distence of four miles to get to the village. Once she was there, she went straight to the residance of her friend, the Lumberjack. She told him of what the Fisher had done, and of the importence of teaching him a lesson. Finally, she asked for his assistince. The Lumberjack's appeerence was stern at first, but he soon agreed to help. They would teach the Fisher their own lesson about balence!

1. _____   3. _____   5. _____

2. _____   4. _____   6. _____

B. Writing Activity

Write a paragraph about a time when you or someone you know played a trick on someone else. Use four words from your spelling list.

_____

_____

_____

_____

_____

_____

_____

_____

_____

_____

LC 1.5 Spell roots, suffixes, prefixes, contractions, and syllable constructions correctly.

- *Its*, *their*, and *your* are **possessive pronouns**. *It's*, *they're*,
  and *you're* are **contractions**. These possessive pronouns and
  contractions are **homophones**, words that sound the same but
  are spelled differently.
- Contractions always use apostrophes.

**Rewrite each sentence. Use possessive pronouns, homophones,
and contractions correctly.**

1. The fisher tricks some people on there way to the market.

   _____

2. He stands their next to the log bridge and shakes it.

   _____

3. There likely to be frightened by the shaky log.

   _____

4. They will think that their going to fall into the river.

   _____

5. They could lose there merchandise or even drown.

   _____

6. "Put some of you're baskets down before you cross," the fisher says.

   _____

   _____

7. He tells the others to leave some of there food before crossing the log.

   _____

   _____

8. As they go to the market, there easily tricked.

   _____

9. However, on they're way home, they see nothing wrong with the bridge.

   _____

   _____

10. They decide that there going to trick the fisher.

    _____

CA **LC 1.0** Written and Oral English Language Conventions

© Macmillan/McGraw-Hill

Name _____

- *Its*, *their*, and *your* are **possessive pronouns**. *It's*, *they're*, and *you're* are **contractions**. These possessive pronouns and contractions are **homophones**.
- The word *there* means "in that place." It is a homophone of *they're* and *their*.
- Do not confuse possessive pronouns with contractions.

Circle all mistakes in the use of possessive pronouns, homophones, and contractions. Then rewrite the passage.

This play is an original trickster story. It's main character is a fisher who is hungry because he can't catch any fish to eat or to sell. He decides to trick people into leaving the goods that there bringing to market on the other side of the river. He does this by pretending that the log bridge is unsteady and that he will hold it in it's place. He tells the people that there in danger if they cross with too much merchandise. So they leave there goods their on the ground before they cross. Then the fisher crosses over and picks up the goods right their where the people left them.

_____

_____

_____

_____

_____

_____

_____

_____

_____

_____

Name _____

An Adventure
By Sheila Ryan

Shayda's breath was a white puff in front of her face. The bitter cold wind whipped into her numbing ears, making an echoing howl. The snowflakes felt like little daggers on her cheeks. Families were huddled together. A big smile spread across Shayda's face as she jumped off the chairlift and headed down the slopes.

1. Read the passage at the top of the page.

2. List some details that Sheila uses to show us the setting.

   _____

3. How does Shayda feel in this setting? _____

4. Continue the story. Write three more sentences that describe Shayda's adventure as she skis down the hill. Include enough detail to show how Shayda responds to the setting.

   _____

   _____

   _____

   _____

   _____

   _____

   _____

   _____

   _____

   _____

   _____

   _____

CA **W 1.0** Writing Strategies

Name _____

> A **suffix** is a word part added to the end of a root word to change its meaning. Adding a suffix sometimes changes the spelling of a root word.
>
> happy + **-ly** = happily   forget + **-able** = forgettable
> argue + **-ment** = argument

Combine the word parts to write a word with a suffix. Remember to make any necessary spelling changes. Then use each word in a sentence.

1. close -ly _____

2. observe -tion _____

_____

3. microscope -ic _____

_____

4. knowledge -able _____

_____

5. concentrate -ion _____

_____

6. care -ful -ly _____

_____

7. happy -ness _____

_____

8. enjoy -able _____

9. strategy -ic _____

_____

10. beauty -ful _____

_____

© Macmillan/McGraw-Hill

| specimens | transferred | murky | dormant |
| biology | scoured | research | observer |

Choose the word that best replaces the underlined word or words. Then write the word on the line.

1. If you are curious about <u>the study of living things,</u> you can make amazing discoveries. _____

2. First you must become <u>someone who watches everything around you</u>.

   _____

3. Your <u>investigations</u> might take you to a park or even to a lake, where you can study life under the water. _____

4. Sometimes a lake will look <u>as though it has no activity</u>, but it is really filled with life. _____

5. In the water you may find minerals to be <u>cleaned</u> back in the lab.

   _____

6. Even if the water is <u>thick and dark</u>, you will probably find something fascinating. _____

7. Take <u>samples</u> of the water so that you can study them under a microscope.

   _____

8. After you have <u>moved</u> the samples to a slide, you can examine them.

   _____

 R 1.0 Word Analysis, Fluency, and Systematic Vocabulary Development

Name _____

> Events in a story or steps in an experiment usually happen in chronological order. If you can recognize and follow the **sequence**, you will better understand what will happen next. Words such as *first*, *then*, *next*, *now*, and *finally* help signal the order in which events or steps occur.

Read the scientific method. Label each step of the scientific method below.

Scientific method is specific steps scientists take during an experiment. Scientists try to answer questions they have by performing several tests. By following a specific sequence during different experiments, they are able to determine the answers to their questions.

1. **Initial or First Observation:** Scientists notice something and wonder why.
2. **Gather Information:** Scientists try to find out more.
3. **Hypothesis:** Scientists take their initial observation and create a question that can be tested. A hypothesis should make a prediction of the outcome.
4. **Testing:** Scientists will perform experiments and record data.
5. **Draw a Conclusion:** Using the information from their tests, scientists will compare this data to their hypothesis to see if their prediction is correct or not.

1. Finally I conclude my hypothesis was correct. The birds made a nest to hold their eggs. _____

2. Then I learned more from a book about birds laying eggs in the spring.

   _____

3. First I see two blue birds. One is flying from tree to tree. The other is gathering twigs. It is springtime. _____

4. Next I observe the birds for a week. They choose a large tree branch. The birds gather more twigs and start building a nest. I see three bird eggs.

   _____

5. I predict the birds will make a nest to hold their eggs.

   _____

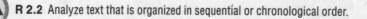

CA R 2.2 Analyze text that is organized in sequential or chronological order.

Name _____

As you read *Hidden Worlds*, fill in the Sequence Charts.

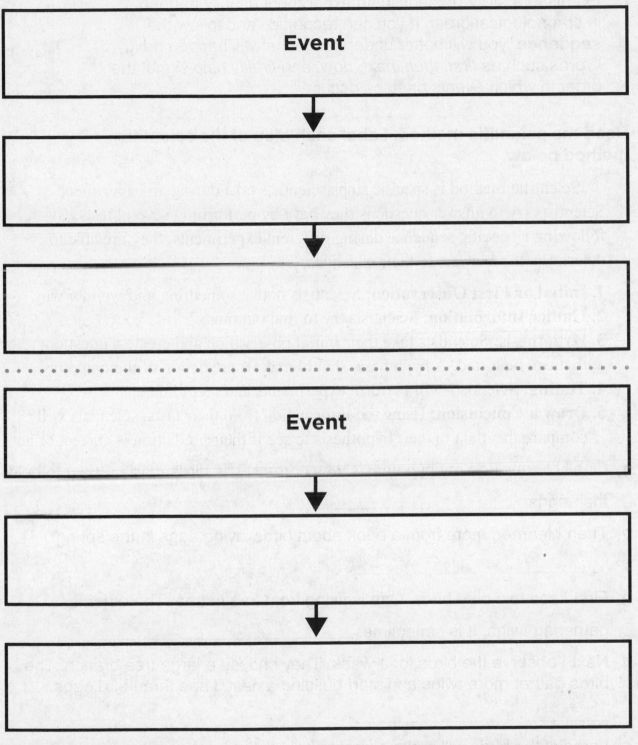

Event

↓

↓

· ·

Event

↓

↓

How does the information you wrote in the Sequence Charts help you
summarize *Hidden Worlds*?

 R 2.2 Analyze text that is organized in sequential or chronological order.

Name _____

As I read, I will pay attention to intonation and phrasing.

	The ocean is big. It covers about two-thirds of Earth. The
11	ocean is also deep—very deep. The ocean's average depth is
22	more than 2 miles (3 kilometers). At its deepest, it goes down
32	nearly 7 miles (11 kilometers). That's taller than Mount
39	Everest.
40	Think of a place where animals live. You might think of
51	a forest or grassland. But what about the ocean? In fact, the
63	ocean makes up most of Earth's habitat. But to this day, most
75	of the deep ocean has never been explored.
83	For centuries, people thought that the bottom of the deep
93	ocean was lifeless. It is very cold in the deep, dark ocean. No
106	light reaches the bottom. And water is heavy. All that water
117	presses down hard on the sea floor. How could anything live
128	down there?
130	But then scientists began exploring the deep. What they
139	found shocked them. On the deep sea floor, they discovered
149	a world beyond their wildest imagination. It is a strange
159	world teeming with bizarre life. 164

Comprehension Check

1. What is it like at the bottom of the ocean? **Main Idea and Details**

2. Why has not much of the deep ocean been explored? **Main Idea and Details**

	Words Read	–	Number of Errors	=	Words Correct Score
First Read		–		=	
Second Read		–		=	

R 1.1 Read aloud narrative and expository text fluently and accurately and with appropriate pacing, **intonation**, and expression.

Name _____

When you read poetry, pay attention to the poem's **rhyme scheme** and **rhythm**. The rhyme scheme is a pattern of words that have the same ending sound, such as *light* and *tight*. Rhythm is the regular repetition of accented or stressed syllables in the lines of a poem. Rhythm gives the poem a steady beat, almost like that of music.

A. In the poem below, fill in the blanks by choosing a word from the list that completes the rhyme scheme. Write the word on the lines provided.

right	round	glow	roar

1. We're in the rocket, set to go.

   The lift-off lights begin to _____.

2. The engines rumble, then they _____.

   Can we still run right out the door?

3. The spacecraft rolls from left to _____.

   And soon we rocket out of sight.

4. But wait! It's over. We're all safe and sound.

   Oh, it was just the simulator spinning _____.

B. Identify the rhythm in these lines of the poem. Underline the accented syllables.

   The spacecraft rolls from left to right.
   And soon we rocket out of sight.
   But wait! It's over. We're all safe and sound.
   Oh, it was just the simulator spinning round.

R 2.0 Reading Comprehension (Focus on Informational Materials)

Many words in English have ancient **Greek or Latin roots**. Sometimes Latin or Greek word parts create a word family, or a group of words with a common feature or pattern. For example, the Greek root *geo* means "earth." The words *geography*, *geology*, *geographer*, *geode*, *geometry*, and *geometric* form a word family based on the words' Greek root *geo*.

Origin	Greek	Latin	Greek	Latin	Latin
Word part	bio	dict	tele	man	terr
Meaning	life	speak	far away	hand	earth

Look at the Latin and Greek word parts above. Choose the word in parentheses that best fits with the other two words to form a word family. Then write the word on the line.

1. bionic   biography   (biosphere/bicker)   _____

2. dictate   dictation   (dice/dictionary)   _____

3. telethon   telephone   (telescope/territory)   _____

4. manner   maneuver   (manicure/main)   _____

5. diction   dictator   (decorate/edict)   _____

6. manual   manufacture   (manuscript/mane)   _____

7. terrarium   terrestrial   (terrible/terrace)   _____

8. television   telegram   (telecast/teller)   _____

9. biology   biologist   (bisect/biographer)   _____

10. telescopic   telepathy   (telegraph/tale)   _____

R 1.4 Know abstract, derived roots and affixes from Greek and Latin and use this knowledge to analyze the meaning of complex words (e.g., *controversial*).

Name _____

Using the Word Study Steps

1. **LOOK** at the word.

2. **SAY** the word aloud.

3. **STUDY** the letters in the word.

4. **WRITE** the word.

5. **CHECK** the word.
   Did you spell the word right?
   If not, go back to step 1.

**A. Circle the spelling words in this puzzle. Each word appears
once. Words may read forward, backward, upward, downward,
or diagonally.**

```
E  G  S  F  I  N  A  L  L  Y  M  Q  C  E  Y  H
E  S  I  W  A  C  M  Q  L  I  R  I  U  L  S  S
R  A  C  T  I  V  I  T  Y  C  P  G  E  O  T  E
U  F  A  A  R  D  N  U  I  O  G  T  F  F  E  R
P  E  F  E  R  E  M  F  C  D  E  N  N  L  V  I
T  T  T  E  R  S  I  S  Y  L  G  O  B  T  E  O
I  Y  I  A  K  T  O  L  P  R  I  A  S  C  N  U
O  C  P  W  N  R  L  M  L  T  T  U  I  K  T  S
N  P  E  E  C  U  O  U  C  R  O  G  C  T  U  U
A  E  I  I  F  C  F  E  O  I  R  V  K  I  A  A
E  C  M  E  K  T  R  F  R  E  D  M  N  B  L  L
S  P  R  U  E  I  M  U  L  I  D  V  E  M  L  L
A  A  D  G  D  O  F  L  T  R  P  O  S  E  Y  Y
C  G  R  I  C  N  A  O  P  Y  I  X  S  R  N  H
P  O  S  I  T  I  O  N  K  E  N  Y  G  T  O  D
F  T  Y  C  I  A  E  N  R  M  S  P  I  P  B  M
```

B. List the words below as you find them in the puzzle.

1. _____   6. _____   11. _____   16. _____

2. _____   7. _____   12. _____   17. _____

3. _____   8. _____   13. _____   18. _____

4. _____   9. _____   14. _____   19. _____

5. _____   10. _____   15. _____   20. _____

LC 1.5 Spell roots, suffixes, prefixes, contractions, and
syllable constructions correctly.

© Macmillan/McGraw-Hill

Name _____

A. Circle the misspelled words in the passage. Write the words correctly on the lines below.

Every time I get near flowers, I sneeze. Apperently I'm allerdgic to them. It isn't serrious, but it does limit my favorite activitie—observing plants and animals. Mom says I may eventualy outgrow the problem. I hope so. One day I want to have a possition as a biologist.

1. _____   3. _____   5. _____

2. _____   4. _____   6. _____

B. Imagine you are a scientist. Describe what your day is like. What do you study? What do you do? Use at least four spelling words in your description.

_____

_____

_____

_____

_____

_____

_____

_____

_____

LC 1.5 Spell roots, suffixes, prefixes, contractions, and syllable constructions correctly.

Name _____

- A **clause** has a subject and predicate.
- An **independent clause** can stand alone as a sentence.
- A **dependent clause** cannot stand alone as a sentence.

A. Read each clause. Tell whether it is an independent clause or a dependent clause.

1. When the scientists looked through the microscope _____

   _____

2. We saw different kinds of plants on the nature walk _____

   _____

3. Because she loved being outdoors _____

4. Before we explored the pond _____

5. We collected samples of leaves and mushrooms _____

   _____

B. Find the dependent clause in each sentence and write it on the line.

6. Before we hiked, we packed our backpacks. _____

7. We gather leaves and soil when we go on nature field trips.

   _____

8. Since John was an expert on volcanoes, he was invited to study one that

   had just erupted. _____

9. You can use a magnifying glass if you want to see something closer.

   _____

10. After a volcano erupts, life eventually returns to the surrounding areas.

    _____

LC 1.1 Identify and correctly use prepositional phrases, appositives, and independent and dependent clauses; use transitions and conjunctions to connect ideas.

© Macmillan/McGraw-Hill

Name _____

Read the paragraph below. Rewrite the paragraph correctly on the lines provided. Be sure each dependent clause is combined with an independent clause. Set off appositives with commas. Correct any punctuation and capitalization errors.

When Hector was young. He knew he wanted to be a scientist. He wanted to become a scientist because he liked to study nature? He learned how to dive. So that he could collect specimens or samples from the ocean. By scrutinizing or examining the specimens scientists can learn how living things survive. do you think science is interesting. If you do. Study science like hector did. Then you can become a scientist, too

_____

_____

_____

_____

_____

_____

_____

LC 1.1 Identify and correctly use prepositional phrases, appositives,
and independent and dependent clauses; use transitions and
conjunctions to connect ideas.
LC 1.4 Use correct capitalization.

Hidden Worlds • Grade 5/Unit 5   **263**

Name _____

1. **Read:**

   <u>STATEMENT 1</u>: Whales are powerful.

   > **EVIDENCE A:** Whales are the largest mammals on the planet.
   >
   > **EVIDENCE B:** When whales breach and let their tails hit the water, they create large waves that can make nearby boats rock.
   >
   > **EVIDENCE C:** With shiny grey eyes and soft skin, whales look as though they'd make beautiful pets.

2. **Circle** the evidence (above) that shows **Statement 1** is true.

3. **Read:**

   <u>STATEMENT 2</u>: I had fun at the amusement park.

   > **EVIDENCE A:** The fourth time I rode the largest rollercoaster I had my hands in the air the whole time; I felt the wind pound into my mouth, which stayed open in laughter.
   >
   > **EVIDENCE B:** My father stepped in gum while we were waiting in line.
   >
   > **EVIDENCE C:** My older brother won three stuffed animals and gave them to me; I kept one and gave the other two to these little kids who loved them.

4. **Circle** the evidence (above) that shows **Statement 2** is true.

CA W 1.0 Writing Strategies

Name _____

Homophones are words that sound alike but that have different spellings and different meanings. For example, the words *flour* and *flower* sound alike, but *flour* is used to make bread, and a *flower* is the bloom of a plant.

A. Choose the word that best completes each sentence. Circle the correct word.

1. They took a (poll/pole) to see which brand of cereal people liked best.

2. She did not like to (waist/waste) time watching television.

3. Dad ate toast with red (current/currant) jelly for breakfast.

4. My aunt is running for city (counsel/council).

5. We waited at the (peer/pier) for the boat to arrive.

6. Her (presence/presents) was very important at the meeting.

7. Who is going to (peal/peel) all of these potatoes?

8. The hotel (sweet/suite) was too expensive.

B. Write a sentence for each homophone.

9. accept: _____

_____

10. except: _____

_____

11. affect: _____

_____

12. effect: _____

_____

Name _____

A. From each pair of words below, circle the word that best completes the sentence. Then write the correct word on the line provided.

1. Snakes are (predators/reptiles) because they live by hunting and eating

   other animals. _____

2. There are about 30 (brands/species) of rattlesnake. _____

3. A rattler shakes its tail as a warning before (fleeing/lunging) toward you.

   _____

4. You can (survive/avoid) a snake bite if you get help right away.

   _____

5. Snakes can feel another animal approaching because the ground

   (vibrates/twists). _____

6. Rattlesnakes often blend in with their (surroundings/forests), which

   makes them hard to see. _____

7. The hikers were (unprepared/alert) after rattlesnakes were spotted on the

   trail. _____

8. A rattlesnake shoots poison through its fangs when it bites its

   (prey/venom). _____

B. Write new sentences for two of the vocabulary words used above. Then underline the vocabulary word.

9. _____

   _____

10. _____

   _____

 R 1.0 Word Analysis, Fluency, and Systematic Vocabulary Development

Name _____

The **main idea** is the most important point an author makes in the story. **Details** are facts that support this main idea and are found throughout the story. By recognizing the main idea and details, you will be able to easily remember the most important information you read in a story.

The introductory paragraphs below come from *Rattlers!* Read the paragraphs and answer the questions about the main idea and supporting details.

Rattlesnakes have a bad reputation. No wonder! They look mean. They sound spooky. And you know about their nasty bite. But mostly they're misunderstood. So here is all you ever wanted to know about rattlesnakes.

They are a group of snakes that have what no other snakes have: rattle-tipped tails. They also have thick bodies, wide heads, cat-like eyes, and long, hollow fangs that fold away when they're not needed. Their dull colors and patchy patterns help them blend with their surroundings.

1. After reading the paragraphs, think about the main idea of *Rattlers!* Circle the letter of the correct main idea.

   a. Rattlesnakes are poisonous snakes that eat other animals.

   b. Rattlesnakes have a bad reputation because they are misunderstood.

   c. People must be brave to study rattlesnakes in the wild.

2. List three details about the characteristics of rattlesnakes that support the main idea.

   a. _____

   _____

   b. _____

   _____

   c. _____

   _____

R 2.3 Discern main ideas and concepts presented in texts, identifying and assessing evidence that supports those ideas.

Name _____

As you read a section of *Rattlers!*, fill in the Main Idea and Details Chart.

Main Idea	Details

How does the information you wrote in this Main Idea and Details Chart help you summarize the section of *Rattlers!* you chose?

 R 2.3 Discern main ideas and concepts presented in texts, identifying and assessing evidence that supports those ideas.

Name _____

As I read, I will pay attention to intonation and phrasing.

	Sea snakes live in the waters of the Indian and Pacific
11	oceans. Since snakes are cold-blooded and depend on warmth
20	from their **surroundings**, their range is limited to the warm
30	tropics and nearby seas. Many live near coral reefs, those
40	stony underwater ridges that attract sea life of all kinds.
50	The total number of snake **species** is over 2,700. There are
61	only about 50 species of true sea snakes. But sea snakes may
73	be the most numerous of all snakes.
80	Most sea snakes are from two feet to a little more than
92	three feet long. A few grow to about eight feet. Most sea
104	snakes have slender bodies that help them move through the
114	water easily.
116	Living in the sea is a challenge for the sea snakes. They
128	have adapted to the sea in several ways. One way is through
140	their shape. 142

Comprehension Check

1. Why do sea snakes have to live in warm waters? **Main Idea and Details**

2. What is one way that sea snakes have adapted to living in water? **Main Idea and Details**

	Words Read	−	Number of Errors	=	Words Correct Score
First Read		−		=	
Second Read		−		=	

R 1.1 Read aloud narrative and expository text fluently and accurately and with appropriate **pacing**, intonation, and expression.

Rattlers! • Grade 5/Unit 5   **269**

Name _____

Legends are stories that come down from the past and are based on the traditions of a people or region. The **hero** is the main character in a legend, who often does something brave to help others. **Personification** is the assignment of human characteristics to an animal, a thing, or an idea.

Read the following passage from "How Poison Came into the World." Answer the questions on the lines provided.

Long ago, when the Earth was young, the Choctaw people loved to swim in the cool waters of the bayou. But the Choctaw had to be very careful when swimming, because a poisonous plant grew in the heart of the bayou. This plant lived below the surface of the water, so swimmers could not see it until it was too late.

The plant, however, did not want to hurt his friends the Choctaw. As more people fell ill, the poor plant became sadder and sadder. Finally, he decided to give away his poison. The plant called the chiefs of the wasps and snakes to meet with him. He asked them to take his poison.

1. Who is the hero in "How Poison Came into the World"? Explain your answer.

_____

_____

2. How is the plant personified? _____

_____

3. How does the legend reflect a certain region or people? _____

_____

4. What sacrifice do you think the plant will make? _____

_____

_____

5. What is the point of this legend? _____

_____

© Macmillan/McGraw-Hill

 R 2.0 Reading Comprehension (Focus on Informational Materials)

> **Context clues** restate what other words mean.
> As you read, you can use context clues to help you define
> unfamiliar words.

**Look for context clues to help you define the underlined word in
each sentence. Then write the meaning of the underlined word on
the line provided.**

1. Many <u>species</u>, or kinds, of rattlesnake are found in the United States.

   _____

2. A rattlesnake shoots <u>venom</u>, or poison, through its fangs when it bites.

   _____

3. Rattlers blend in with their <u>surroundings</u> because their dull colors and

   patchy skin match their environment. _____

4. The fangs of a rattlesnake fold away when they're <u>unnecessary</u>, or not

   needed. _____

5. Rattlesnakes use <u>pits</u>, or dents, on their heads to sense the body heat of

   other animals. _____

6. When a rattlesnake shakes its tail, the rattle <u>vibrates</u> and makes noise.

   _____

7. Snakes can move quickly, even though they just <u>slither</u>, or slide, along.

   _____

8. Some animals are not <u>bothered</u>, or harmed, by rattlesnake venom.

   _____

 R 1.0 Word Analysis, Fluency, and Systematic Vocabulary Development

Using the Word Study Steps

1. LOOK at the word.
2. SAY the word aloud.
3. STUDY the letters in the word.

4. WRITE the word.
5. CHECK the word.
   Did you spell the word right?
   If not, go back to step 1.

Fill-Ins

A. Fill in the missing letters of each word to form a spelling word.

1. su____ ____e
2. sw____ ____t
3. p____ ____r
4. p____ ____r
5. cur____en____
6. curr____ ____ts
7. man____ ____r

8. ma____ ____r
9. po____e
10. pol____
11. station____ ____y
12. stati____ ____er____
13. wai____ ____
14. was____ ____

15. pr____ ____
16. pr____ ____
17. prese____ ____s
18. pre____e____c____
19. coun____i____
20. cou____s____l

Make a Puzzle

B. Make up a puzzle of your own, using the space on this page. Give it to someone else to solve. Be sure to include at least five spelling words in your puzzle.

 LC 1.5 Spell roots, suffixes, prefixes, contractions, and syllable constructions correctly.

Name _____

A. Circle the misspelled words in the passage. Write the words correctly on the lines below.

Wesley never exercised, and his mannor of dieting was poor. Luckily, the fruits that he grew were not only suite but healthful, too. He grew grapes and currents. Within a few weeks, his waste shrank by two inches. The boys who had teased him before now came and sought his counsil. People in the neighborhood went out of their way just to be in his presents.

1. _____   3. _____   5. _____

2. _____   4. _____   6. _____

B. Writing Activity

Write a paragraph about a summer project that you would like to try. Use four words from your spelling list.

_____

_____

_____

_____

_____

_____

_____

_____

_____

_____

_____

_____

LC 1.5 Spell roots, suffixes, prefixes, contractions, and syllable constructions correctly.

Name _____

> An **independent clause** can stand alone as a sentence.
>
> **Example:** *The snake slithered behind the rock.*
>
> A **dependent clause** begins with a conjunction such as *after,* *because, when, if, since, though,* or *where.* It cannot stand alone as a sentence.
>
> **Example:** *when it saw me*
>
> A **complex sentence** has an independent clause and one or more dependent clauses.
>
> **Example:** *The snake slithered behind the rock when it saw me.*

A. Read each sentence. Circle the conjunction and underline the dependent clause.

1. Because he has several pet snakes, my brother is the family expert on reptiles.

2. I checked out a book about lizards so I could learn more about them.

3. Don't be afraid to ask a question if you aren't sure what to do.

4. After talking to the veterinarian, I was better able to care for my dog.

B. Combine the independent and dependent clauses to write a complex sentence.

5. After the speaker was finished. I asked a question. _____

_____

6. The librarian helped me find a book about alligators. When I had to write a report. _____

_____

7. My dad knows a lot about nature. Because he is a park ranger. _____

_____

8. I like to record things I see. So I keep a journal. _____

_____

LC 1.1 Identify and correctly use prepositional phrases, appositives, and independent and dependent clauses; use transitions and conjunctions to connect ideas.

© Macmillan/McGraw-Hill

> A **dependent clause** cannot stand alone as a sentence. It must be joined to an **independent clause**.

Rewrite the paragraph. Fix any sentence fragments by combining independent and dependent clauses. Correct any errors in punctuation or capitalization.

I want to become a biologist. Because I love studying plants and animals. When a Biologist visited my science class. I asked her what i needed to do to prepare for a career in science. She told me that scientists are curious They ask lots of questions? Then they do experiments and research. To find the answers to their questions. She told me i was off to a great start. Because Im not afraid to ask questions. She also recommended a book titled Becoming a biologist and a magazine article titled On your way to a Career in science."

_____

_____

_____

_____

_____

_____

_____

_____

_____

_____

_____

LC 1.1 Identify and correctly use prepositional phrases, appositives, and independent and dependent clauses; use transitions and conjunctions to connect ideas.
LC 1.3 Use a colon to separate hours and minutes and to introduce a list; use quotation marks around the exact words of a speaker and titles of poems, songs, short stories, and so forth.

Rattlers! • **Grade 5/Unit 5** **275**

1. **Read:**

   My father should give me a ride to school.

2. **Think:** What are two questions you could ask in order to find **relevant evidence** to support this statement?

   Examples:

   How far away is school from your house?

   Why can't you take a school bus or public transportation?

3. **Write** two questions you could ask in order to find **relevant evidence** to support these statements:

   <u>**Statement 1:**</u> Tennis is the most interesting sport to watch.

   Example Question: What makes tennis interesting?

   Question 1: _____

   Question 2: _____

   <u>**Statement 2:**</u> Poetry is usually hard to understand.

   Question 1: _____

   Question 2: _____

   <u>**Statement 3:**</u> Movies should not be rated.

   Question 1: _____

   Question 2: _____

© Macmillan/McGraw-Hill

Name _____

A **prefix** is an affix added to the front of a base or root word.
When you add a prefix, you change the meaning of the word.
In- means "without; not."
Dis- means "the opposite or lack of; not."
Mis- means "bad or wrong."
Pre- means "before."

**Add *in-*, *dis-*, *mis-*, or *pre-* to each of the words in the sentences
below. Use context clues to help you decide which prefix to use.**

1. My teacher _____ approves of talking in class because it disturbs
   the other students.

2. A lumpy mattress can cause _____ comfort for your back.

3. You may need to _____ wash new clothes before you wear them.

4. The outfielder _____ judged the fly ball and did not make the catch.

5. You should not _____ judge food before you try it because you
   might actually like it.

6. My father _____ heats the oven before he puts the food in.

7. Rivals often _____ trust each other because they think the other
   person is trying to trick them.

8. The cheap toys were _____ expensive, so Mom agreed to buy them.

9. I _____ understood my teacher and wrote the wrong spelling word.

10. It is _____ honest to cheat on a test.

observed	inhibit	investigating
conquer	insight	

A. Complete each sentence by choosing the best word from the box.

1. One doctor is _____ how diseases spread among students at school.

2. She has _____ hundreds of students in the classroom.

3. She believes that getting plenty of sleep can _____ illnesses.

4. This _____ might help students stay healthy.

5. Studies like this are helping to _____ disease.

B. Choose three vocabulary words. Write a sentence of your own for each of these words.

6. _____

_____

7. _____

_____

8. _____

_____

LC 1.5 Spell roots, suffixes, prefixes, contractions, and syllable constructions correctly.

Name _____

> A **generalization** is a statement about all people, things, or ideas.
> Words such as *all*, *every*, *most*, and *never* can help you identify
> generalizations.

Read the passage, and answer the questions.

Penguins live in the Southern Hemisphere. Most penguins live in places far from people. Some live on the southern tip of South America. Some live on islands in the Pacific Ocean. A few build nests in Antarctica.

There are 17 species of penguins. The Little Blue Penguin is the smallest species. It weighs about two pounds. The largest species, the Emperor Penguin, can weigh up to 80 pounds. Although they look different in some ways, all penguins share certain features. They all are covered with feathers, are warm-blooded, and have webbed feet. Like all birds, penguins have wings. However, penguins never fly. Instead, they use their flipper-like wings to dive deep beneath the water.

1. Which statement is a generalization?

   a. Penguins live in South America.

   b. Most penguins live in places far from people.

   c. Some penguins build nests Antarctica.

2. Which statement is a generalization?

   a. There are 17 species of penguins.

   b. The Little Blue Penguin is the smallest species.

   c. All penguins are covered with feathers

3. Which statement is NOT a generalization?

   a. Some penguins eat krill.

   b. Penguins never fly.

   c. All penguins have wings.

4. Write one generalization about penguins.

_____

R 2.4 Draw inferences, conclusions, or generalizations about text
and support them with textual evidence and prior knowledge.

Name _____

As you read *These Robots Are Wild!*, fill in the Generalizations
Chart.

Important Information	Generalization

How does the information you wrote in the Generalizations Chart help
you evaluate *These Robots Are Wild!*?

CA R 2.4 Draw inferences, conclusions, or generalizations about text
and support them with textual evidence and prior knowledge.

© Macmillan/McGraw-Hill

Name _____

As I read, I will pay attention to phrasing.

	Do you have strong feelings about something? Do others
9	feel differently? Often this can happen in families. Maybe
18	family members ask you to help keep your home clean.
28	They say that you live in the home, and it's disrespectful
39	for you to ignore your responsibility. On the other hand, the
50	mess does not bother you. You think that those who are
61	preoccupied with the mess should be the ones to clean it up.
73	Or your family members may point out that the ones who
84	pay the bills should make the rules of the house. You think
96	that everyone in the house should help make the rules.
106	A debate like this may go back and forth for some time.
118	Each person tries to convince the others that he or she
129	is right. In a situation like this one, no one is really right
142	or wrong. Yet each person wants to win. What is the
153	answer? 154

Comprehension Check

1. Who do some family members think should make the rules? **Main Idea and Details**

2. What is a debate? **Relevant Facts and Details**

	Words Read	–	Number of Errors	=	Words Correct Score
First Read		–		=	
Second Read		–		=	

 R 1.1 Read aloud narrative and expository text fluently and accurately and with appropriate pacing, intonation, and expression.

These Robots Are Wild!
Grade 5/Unit 5

Name _____

A **library** often holds more than collections of books and magazines. Due to advances in technology, information can be stored and presented in many different forms. To use a library or **media center** successfully, choose the correct resources.

Choose the resource from the chart that would provide useful information for each item below. Write the name of the resource on the line provided.

Sample of Media Center Resources
Thomas Pakenham's book of photographs about trees around the world
online encyclopedia, key words "wildfire" and "containment"
CD entitled *The Music of the Brazilian Rain Forest*
video documentary called *Three Forest Biomes and the Animals That Live in Them*
print encyclopedia, volume B, article about common trees
CD-ROM entitled *Maps, Geography, and the Environment*

1. Which resource would you use to read articles about these common trees in the United States: black cherry, box elder, black willow?

_____

2. Which resource would you use to hear what a typical day in a rain forest sounds like? _____

_____

3. Which resource would you use to find pictures of a tree named "General Sherman" in California and a tree called a "dancing lime" in Germany? _____

_____

4. Which resource would you use to learn about techniques used to control wildfires? _____

_____

© Macmillan/McGraw-Hill

 R 2.0 Reading Comprehension

Name _____

Problem/Solution Writing Frame

A. Summarize *These Robots Are Wild!* Use the Problem/Solution Writing Frame below.

Scientists are busy creating robots to help solve difficult **problems**.

One problem is finding people in collapsed buildings after an earthquake. **To solve this problem**, scientists are studying animals such as _____

_____

_____

_____.

This is because _____

_____

_____

_____.

As a result, robots made like these animals will _____

_____

_____

_____.

B. Rewrite the completed summary on another sheet of paper. Keep it as a model for writing a summary of an article or selection using this text structure.

CA R 2.0 Reading Comprehension

These Robots Are Wild!
Grade 5/Unit 5   **283**

The root of a word is the part that carries its main meaning. The roots of many English words originally came from Greek or Latin. Knowing **Greek and Latin roots** can help you figure out the meaning of unfamiliar words.

Root	Meaning	Language
astr	star	Greek
chron	time	Greek
gen	birth	Greek
sci	know	Latin
san	health	Latin
aud	hear	Latin

Use the chart above to help you choose the word in parentheses that is being described.

1. This is a noun that means "the time order in which events occur." (chronology, covert) _____

2. This is the study of the history of births in families. (pharmacology, genealogy) _____

3. This is a large building or room where people listen to concerts. (auditorium, concerto) _____

4. This adjective means "awake and able to think and know." (conscious, determined) _____

5. This adjective means "free from germs that cause illness." (laundered, sanitary) _____

6. This is the study of objects in space. (anthropology, astronomy)
_____

© Macmillan/McGraw-Hill

 R 1.4 Know abstract, derived roots and affixes from Greek and Latin and use this knowledge to analyze the meaning of complex words (e.g., *controversial*).

Name _____

Using the Word Study Steps

1. LOOK at the word.
2. SAY the word aloud.
3. STUDY the letters in the word.

4. WRITE the word.
5. CHECK the word.
   Did you spell the word right?
   If not, go back to step 1.

A. Find and Circle

**Find and circle each of the spelling words in this puzzle. Words
may read forward, backward, upward, downward, or diagonally.**

```
D P R E J U D G E S K G I E D D P L H E
Z I E C I T S U J N I L N V E I G U S T
I R S E G D U J S I M G C I V S G A A I
L I Z H P R E V I E W B O S O C E S W N
D W X D O D I S A B L E R N R O N T E I
R H X T N N A Y C D L F R E P M E A R F
Y D B O O J E C P J R N E P P F K E P E
Y E B O S I D S R E F G C X A O A H M D
D I S M O U N T T E N K T E S R T E D N
M I S U N D E R S T A N D N I T S R G I
T C E N N O C S I D U R N I D U I P K J
M I S T R U S T D I S C O L O R M D C A
```

B. List each of the words below as you find them in the puzzle.

1. _____
2. _____
3. _____
4. _____
5. _____
6. _____
7. _____

8. _____
9. _____
10. _____
11. _____
12. _____
13. _____
14. _____

15. _____
16. _____
17. _____
18. _____
19. _____
20. _____

CA **LC 1.5** Spell roots, suffixes, prefixes, contractions, and syllable
constructions correctly.

These Robots Are Wild!
Grade 5/Unit 5   **285**

A. Circle the misspelled words in the passage. Write the words correctly on the lines below.

Many people are mistakin about what they can do to help protect
nature. They think that the destruction of our environment is an injustis,
but they don't know how they can help. In fact, there are plenty of easy
and inexpencive ways to take action. Some people disobay recycling laws
because they don't know any better! You can tell people who litter or
pollute that you disaproove. Don't prejuge others, but take some time to
learn what you can do to help.

1. _____   3. _____   5. _____

2. _____   4. _____   6. _____

B. Writing Activity

Write a paragraph about things that you can do to help protect
nature in your area. Use four words from your spelling list.

_____

_____

_____

_____

_____

_____

_____

_____

_____

_____

_____

 LC 1.5 Spell roots, suffixes, prefixes, contractions, and syllable
constructions correctly.

- For adjectives ending in *e*, drop the *e* before adding *-er* or *-est*.
- For adjectives ending in a consonant and *y*, change the *y* to *i* before adding *-er* or *-est*.
- For one-syllable adjectives that have a single vowel before the final consonant, double the final consonant before adding *-er* or *-est*.

Read each sentence. Rewrite it with the correct adjective form.

1. One of the healing plants was <u>leafy</u> than the others.

   _____

   _____

2. Even the <u>tiny</u> insects can teach scientists important things about nature.

   _____

   _____

3. He felt like the <u>lucky</u> science teacher in the country.

   _____

4. E. O. Wilson worked to make our planet <u>healthy</u> than it was.

   _____

   _____

5. Neither Clark nor Lewis was <u>brave</u> than the other.

   _____

6. Lewis and Clark are two of the <u>brave</u> men in history.

   _____

7. Keeping a journal is <u>easy</u> for some people than it is for others.

   _____

   _____

8. The men thought it was <u>hot</u> today than it was yesterday.

   _____

   _____

© Macmillan/McGraw-Hill

Name _____

Identify the errors involving adjectives that compare in the following paragraph. Rewrite the paragraph, correcting any errors in grammar, capitalization, and punctuation.

Welcome to the Columbus history Museum! We have made a few changes. First, we have a large exhibit about lewis and Clark than we did before. Now we room have for a map from 1804. It is the old map in the museum. Also, The lights are bright than before. People say that it is easy to read signs than it was.

_____

_____

_____

_____

_____

_____

_____

_____

_____

_____

_____

_____

_____

_____

_____

_____

LC 1.0 Written and Oral English Language Conventions

Writing Rubric

4 Excellent	3 Good	2 Fair	1 Unsatisfactory
Ideas and Content/ Genre	Ideas and Content/ Genre	Ideas and Content/ Genre	Ideas and Content/ Genre
Organization and Focus	Organization and Focus	Organization and Focus	Organization and Focus
Sentence Structure/ Fluency	Sentence Structure/ Fluency	Sentence Structure/ Fluency	Sentence Structure/ Fluency
Conventions	Conventions	Conventions	Conventions
Word Choice	Word Choice	Word Choice	Word Choice
Voice	Voice	Voice	Voice
Presentation	Presentation	Presentation	Presentation

Name _____

Suffixes are word parts that are added to the end of words to change their meanings. The suffix **-less** means "without." The suffix **-ness** means "the state or act of."

When added to base words, the suffixes **-less** and **-ness** are unaccented syllables. They receive less stress than the base words.

Example: fond + -*ness* = fondness. **Fond** is the accented syllable, while the suffix **-ness** is unaccented.

Use what you know about suffixes to write the meanings of the words in the chart. Then write the words in syllables. Write the accented syllable in capital letters. Follow the example.

Base word + suffix	Meaning	Accented syllable
Example: fearless	without fear, brave	FEAR less
effortless		
fierceness		
stillness		
forgiveness		
meaningless		
harmless		
weakness		
weightlessness		
motionless		
gladness		

© Macmillan/McGraw-Hill

 R 1.0 Word Analysis, Fluency, and Systematic Vocabulary Development

Name _____

| launched | particles | dense | inflate |
| anchored | Civil | scientific | companion |

A. Choose the word from the list above that best completes each sentence. Then write the word on the line.

1. The hot-air balloon soared through the air because it was not

   _____, or held down, to the ground by anything.

2. The balloons soar because the hot air is light and the air surrounding

   it is heavy and _____.

3. People in hot-air balloons are _____ into the sky.

4. The large balloons _____ when they are filled with hot air.

5. The small pieces of matter in air move faster as the air heats. Then the

   _____ spread out, and the balloon rises.

6. During the _____ War, soldiers used balloons to spy.

7. Some people ride in hot-air balloons to do _____ experiments.

8. You and a _____ might enjoy sharing a hot-air balloon ride.

B. Label each statement *True* or *False*.

9. The science club launched the balloon, and it dug deep into the earth.

   _____

10. You can inflate a balloon with hydrogen or hot air. _____

11. The balloon will not move when it is anchored to the ground.

   _____

12. To conduct scientific experiments you must bring a companion.

   _____

© Macmillan/McGraw-Hill

Name _____

A **generalization** is a broad statement about a group made by adding information to your own knowledge and experience.

- Words such as *none*, *always*, and *all* signal generalizations that are universally true.
- Words such as *some*, *usually*, and *almost* signal limited generalizations.

A. Circle the letter of the correct answer to the following questions.

1. Which of the following statements is a generalization?

   a. Some inventions are inspired by nature.

   b. Velcro was inspired by burrs that were stuck to George de Mestral's dog.

   c. It took eight years to perfect the design for Velcro.

2. Read the information about Thomas Edison and Alexander Graham Bell. Then choose the most valid generalization.

   As a child, Thomas Edison asked a lot of questions. Alexander Graham Bell was already inventing by age 14.

   a. Most inventors and scientists wait until they're adults to ask questions.

   b. Few inventors are curious as children.

   c. Many inventors are curious at a young age.

B. Write a valid generalization based on the information given.

3. Science has found cures for many illnesses. Research has also led to artificial limbs that can help people walk. _____

   _____

4. It took eight years to perfect Velcro. It took ten years to develop the machine that produces cellophane. _____

   _____

 R 2.4 Draw inferences, conclusions, or generalizations about text and support them with textual evidence and prior knowledge.

Name _____

As you read *Up in the Air: The Story of Balloon Flight*, fill in the
Generalizations Chart.

Information from Text	
Prior Knowledge	
Generalization	

How does the information you wrote in the Generalizations Chart help
you understand and evaluate the information in *Up in the Air: The Story
of Balloon Flight*?

R 2.4 Draw inferences, conclusions, or generalizations about text
and support them with textual evidence and prior knowledge.

As I read, I will pay attention to pacing.

	It is a beautiful day at the football stadium. Fans fill the
12	seats and wait for the kickoff. Suddenly, a strange shadow
22	appears on the field. People sitting in the upper rows hear
33	a low whirring sound overhead. Floating in the sky is a
44	football-shaped balloon.
47	Most of us have seen them on television during sporting
57	events. They are like silent ships sailing on a sea of sky.
69	These strange-looking balloons are called blimps. They are
77	cousins to the hot-air balloon.
82	Blimps and hot-air balloons are part of a group of flying
93	machines known as lighter-than-air craft. They are filled
101	with gas that weighs less than air.
108	Blimps are also members of the airship family. Just like
118	boats, airships have motors and rudders. The motors give
127	airships speed. The rudders help steer. These additions make
136	airships very different from hot-air balloons. Hot-air balloons
144	have little control over their speed or direction. Airships can
154	even fly against the wind. 159

Comprehension Check

1. Compare and contrast blimps and hot-air balloons. **Compare and Contrast**

2. Where do people commonly see blimps? **Main Idea and Details**

	Words Read	–	Number of Errors	=	Words Correct Score
First Read		–		=	
Second Read		–		=	

R 1.1 Read aloud narrative and expository text fluently and accurately and with appropriate **pacing**, intonation, and expression.

When you read poetry, you often encounter poetic elements such as **similes** and **metaphors**. Similes and metaphors use language to create striking or unexpected images for the reader. These are figures of speech that compare or associate two things. Similes use *like* or *as* in the comparison. Metaphors compare without using *like* or *as*.

Read the poem to answer the following questions.

Balloon Flight Haiku

It floats in the air
like a bird's loosened feather,
drifting among blue.

The azure ocean
above our very heads
is where it sails high.

Unlike a feather,
it is guided by someone
who chooses its course.

1. What similes can you find in the haiku?

   _____

   _____

2. What metaphors can you find in the haiku?

   _____

   _____

3. What comparisons are made in the haiku?

   _____

   _____

   _____

4. Which comparison is not stated directly? How do you know the comparison is made?

   _____

   _____

   _____

R 3.5 Describe the function and effect of common literary devices
(e.g., imagery, **metaphor**, symbolism).

Many English words have roots that originally came from the ancient Greek language. Knowing what the **Greek root** means will help you figure out the meaning of the word.

Root	Meaning
hydro	water
aster/astro	star
dem	people
graph	write
log/logue	word
pod	foot

Use the chart above to help you choose which word is being described in each item below.

1. The lightest gas, this element is found in water and all organic substances.

   (helium, hydrogen) _____

2. This is a noun that means "a conversation, often in a story."

   (dialogue, dialect) _____

3. This object has three "feet." (tricycle, tripod) _____

4. This kind of political system allows the people to vote for their government.

   (democracy, monarchy) _____

5. This is a form of communication that people use to write in Morse code.

   (telephone, telegraph) _____

6. This is the study of the stars and planets. (geology, astronomy)

   _____

CA R 1.4 Know abstract, derived roots and affixes from **Greek** and Latin and use this knowledge to analyze the meaning of complex words (e.g., *controversial*).

Using the Word Study Steps

1. LOOK at the word.
2. SAY the word aloud.
3. STUDY the letters in the word.
4. WRITE the word.
5. CHECK the word.
   Did you spell the word right?
   If not, go back to step 1.

Fill-Ins

A. Fill in the missing letters of each word to form a spelling word.

1. bottom____ ____ ____s
2. cease____ ____ ____s
3. dark____ ____ ____s
4. effort____ ____ ____s
5. empt____ ____ ____ss
6. fea____ ____ess
7. fierc____n____ ____s
8. fon____ ____es____
9. fooli____ ____ ____ess
10. forgiv____ ____ess

11. ful____n____ ____s
12. hope____ ____ss
13. gla____ ____ess
14. mean____ng____ ____ss
15. har____ ____ess
16. moti____ ____l____ss
17. need____ ____ss
18. sti____l____e____s
19. sa____n____s____
20. wea____ ____es____

B. Use the spelling words above to write a poem of at least four lines.

_____

_____

_____

_____

LC 1.5 Spell roots, suffixes, prefixes, contractions, and syllable
constructions correctly.

Up in the Air • **Grade 5/Unit 5** **297**

Name _____

Proofreading

A. Circle the misspelled words in the passage. Write the words correctly on the lines below.

The soldiers stood moshunless in the field. What was so important about a harmliss code? As the darknes crept in, they felt alone. An emptyness came over them as they waited. The mission seemed meaninglis to them. They had no idea that the language they knew so well would play a key part in the weekness of the Japanese army!

1. _____   3. _____   5. _____

2. _____   4. _____   6. _____

Writing Activity

B. Write a paragraph about what you would do if you had a code of your own. Use four words from your spelling list.

_____

_____

_____

_____

_____

_____

_____

_____

_____

_____

_____

_____

 LC 1.5 Spell roots, suffixes, prefixes, contractions, and syllable constructions correctly.

- When you use *more* and *most,* do not use the ending -*er* or -*est.*

Read the paragraphs. Then rewrite each paragraph, correcting any mistakes. Be sure that *more* and *most* are used correctly and that all adjectives are spelled correctly.

When Grandfather was young, he thought that the clouds were most beautifulest in the hills. Being outside was always more pleasanter than being in school. Grandfather was happier of all when he could stay outside

_____

_____

_____

_____

_____

Creating a code is very more difficult, but it is even most difficulter to break a code. In the past, breaking a code was one of the more crucial skills of all. Sometimes governments didn't realize that a code had been broken, and they continued to send their most secretest messages in that code.

_____

_____

_____

_____

_____

_____

_____

Name _____

In the following paragraph, identify the errors in the use of *more* and *most* with adjectives. Then rewrite the paragraph, correcting any mistakes.

    Codes have been used for a long time. Codes are a way to make a message more harder to understand than if the message had been written in everyday language. Some of the most difficultest codes change the order of the letters in words. Other codes use an uncommon language. An example of this type is the Navajo code used during World War II. It was one of the bestest choices because few people know Navajo. No matter how hard the Japanese tried, they could not break this code. Navajo code was one of the most importantest weapons for the United States during World War II.

_____

_____

_____

_____

_____

_____

_____

_____

_____

_____

_____

_____

© Macmillan/McGraw-Hill

LC 1.0 Written and Oral English Language Conventions

Name _____

<u>School Uniforms</u>
By Ethan Green

    Not wearing school uniforms is too stressful for students. My sister Beth is late for school almost every day because she spends so much time deciding what to wear. Clothes cause a lot of arguments between my mother and Beth, too. She begs Mom to buy expensive jeans, but Mom says, "Honey, that's not in our budget." Once, Beth saved up her baby-sitting money for two months to buy a trendy shirt. She spilled a meatball sub down the front and ruined it the first time she wore it. She cried for days about that. If she had to wear a uniform to school, life would be much easier for my sister Beth.

1. Read the paragraph above.

2. Think: What is the **argument** the writer is trying to make?

    What is the **evidence** the writer uses to support his/her argument?

3. Write the argument and evidence on the lines below:

Argument: _____

_____

Evidence: _____

_____

Evidence: _____

_____

Evidence: _____

_____

© Macmillan/McGraw-Hill

The suffix **-ion** means "act or process", or "state or condition."
You must drop the **e** from words that end in silent **e** before adding
-ion. For example, the word **separate** must lose its **e** before you
can add **-ion** to make the word **separation**.

**Add -ion to the words in the box to complete each sentence below.
Remember to drop the silent e before adding -ion.**

concentrate	exhaust	confuse	discuss
elect	decorate	correct	locate

1. The results of the _____ showed that the more experienced candidate won the most votes.

2. The incomplete directions led to _____ among the students.

3. They used the roses as _____ on the parade float.

4. He was so focused during the test that nothing could break his

   _____.

5. Staying up late can lead to _____ if you do not get enough sleep.

6. Although the _____ of the park was marked on the map, she could not find it.

7. The student worked very hard on his paper, and it needed only one small

   _____.

8. When they could not agree, their _____ quickly became an argument.

© Macmillan/McGraw-Hill

CA R 1.0 Word Analysis, Fluency, and Systematic Vocabulary Development

Name _____

A. Select the correct word from the vocabulary words within the parentheses. Then write your choice on the line.

Hurricanes are tropical storms with rain and strong swirling winds. Hurricanes form over the ocean where warm water is (available / beautiful)

_____ as a source of energy. The (property / atmosphere)

_____ surrounding a hurricane uses moisture from the

warm water to power the storm. When a hurricane moves toward land, a

(surge / destruction) _____ of water can cause flooding

in coastal areas. When a hurricane finally makes (waves / contact)

_____ with the land, high winds are a serious threat.

These powerful storms can cause much (destruction / atmosphere)

_____ to (surges / property) _____. The cost

of (contacts / damages) _____ from a hurricane can reach

billions of dollars.

B. Write your own paragraph about hurricanes, using at least three vocabulary words. Then underline each vocabulary word.

_____

_____

_____

_____

_____

_____

_____

Description is an organizational pattern authors sometimes use in textbook writing. Signal words and phrases such as *most important, for example, for instance,* or *to begin with* alert readers about an upcoming list or set of characteristics.

Read the paragraph. Then answer the questions below.

Hurricane Andrew was one of the worst hurricanes to hit the United States. Andrew first formed in the warm waters of the southern Atlantic Ocean in August 1992. To begin with, the storm had winds of only 40 miles per hour. As the storm continued to move over the warm ocean, it gained energy and grew stronger. When the wind speed reached 74 miles per hour, the storm was officially a hurricane and was named Andrew. Then Andrew's winds climbed to 155 miles per hour! Next, heavy rain moved onshore as Andrew made landfall in southern Florida. Seven inches of rain fell, and storm tides were as high as 17 feet. Hurricane Andrew caused significant destruction to property in the United States. Final damages eventually totaled $25 billion.

1. What is the first fact the author gives about the storm that became Hurricane Andrew? _____

_____

2. What was the initial wind speed of the storm? _____

_____

3. What signal word or phrase does the author use to describe Andrew's wind speed before it became a hurricane? _____

4. The author uses *next* to alert you to what descriptive fact? _____

_____

5. What were the final damage costs? _____

_____

© Macmillan/McGraw-Hill

 R 2.0 Reading Comprehension (Focus on Informational Materials)

Name _____

As you read *Hurricanes*, fill in the Description Chart.

Signal Words		Descriptive Facts
	→	

How does the information you wrote in the Description Chart help you
analyze the text structure of *Hurricanes*?

© Macmillan/McGraw-Hill

Name _____

As I read, I will pay attention to intonation and phrasing.

	The Brodie family—mother, father, two boys, three cats,
9	a dog, and an iguana—was watching television on Monday
19	evening, May 3, 1999. An afternoon thunderstorm was
25	creating tornadoes to the southwest of their home in the
35	suburbs of Oklahoma City, Oklahoma. It looked as if a big
46	tornado was headed their way.
51	The Brodies knew that the best place to be during a
62	tornado is in the basement or under heavy furniture in a
73	small room without windows. They went into their
81	underground tornado shelter.
84	The tornado that swept through heavily populated
91	Oklahoma City on the night of May 3 was classified as
101	an F5 tornado, the most powerful ever recorded.
108	A group in another underground shelter felt the tornado
117	pass directly over their heads. The walls of the shelter started
128	to vibrate. Then, according to a witness, the group heard
138	"one big crack" as the house above them was lifted off its
150	foundation.
151	The tornado was part of the Oklahoma Tornado Outbreak
160	of May 1999. 162

Comprehension Check

1. What should you do to stay safe during a tornado? **Main Idea and Details**

2. Where did the Brodies keep safe during the tornado? **Relevant Facts and Details**

	Words Read	–	Number of Errors	=	Words Correct Score
First Read		–		=	
Second Read		–		=	

© Macmillan/McGraw-Hill

 R 1.1 Read aloud narrative and expository text fluently and accurately and with appropriate pacing, **intonation**, and expression.

Name _____

Practice

Literary Elements:
Personification,
Imagery, and
Onomatopoeia

Elements used in poetry include **personification**, or giving human characteristics to an animal, thing, or idea. Another element is **imagery**, or the use of descriptions to create vivid pictures in the reader's mind. An additional element is **onomatopoeia**, or the use of words that imitate the sounds of an object or action.

Read the poems and answer the questions.

Rabbit Mother sings her babies to sleep.
Tells them not to worry about the rain that splashes down,
Or that flash of lighting and sudden crash of thunder.
Her babies safe in a hillside burrow and Rabbit Mother taps her toes.
Waiting out another hurricane.

1. What literary devices does the poem above contain? How do you know?

_____

_____

2. What examples of onomatopoeia are used to describe the hurricane?

_____

Hurricane
Spinning leaves, flowing water.
All rotating together.
Like water spinning down the drain of an enormous bathtub.
Clockwise in the South. Counterclockwise in the North.
No toys, no bubbles.
Only wind and rain, and the hope that soon all will be safely dried
With the fluffy towel of sunshine.

3. What literary device does this poem have? How do you know?

_____

_____

_____

CA R 3.5 Describe the function and effect of common literary devices
(e.g., imagery, metaphor, symbolism).

Hurricanes • Grade 5/Unit 5 **307**

© Macmillan/McGraw-Hill

Words with more than one meaning are **multiple-meaning words**. You can use context clues or other words in the sentence to help you figure out the most appropriate meaning. Sometimes you may need to consult a dictionary to find all the different meanings of the word.

Write a definition of the underlined word based on how it is used in the sentence.

1. When a hurricane's <u>eye</u> passes over you, the wind stops blowing.

   Eye means: _____

   _____.

2. An <u>eye</u> will allow you to see your surroundings.

   Eye means: _____

   _____.

3. Even during the worst of the storm, my mother maintained her <u>image</u> of calm.

   Image means: _____

   _____.

4. The postcard had an <u>image</u> of a very famous painting on it.

   Image means: _____

   _____.

5. A hurricane <u>watch</u> was issued, so we prepared to leave.

   Watch means: _____

   _____.

6. My <u>watch</u> stopped keeping time because the battery died.

   Watch means: _____

   _____.

© Macmillan/McGraw-Hill

CA R 1.0 Word Analysis, Fluency, and Systematic Vocabulary Development

Name _____

Using the Word Study Steps

1. LOOK at the word.

2. SAY the word aloud.

3. STUDY the letters in the word.

4. WRITE the word.

5. CHECK the word.
   Did you spell the word right?
   If not, go back to step 1.

Fill-Ins

A. Fill in the missing letters of each word to form a spelling word.

1. disc____ ____s
2. loca____ ____
3. imp____ ____ss
4. el____ ____t
5. elect____ ____n
6. correc____ ____on
7. decor____ ____e
8. confusi____ ____
9. concentrati____ ____
10. concentra____ ____

11. discus____ ____on
12. loca____ ____ ____n
13. impress____ ____ ____
14. corre____ ____
15. confu____ ____
16. decora____ ____on
17. estim____ ____ion
18. exhau____ ____
19. exhaust____ ____ ____
20. estim____ ____e

Alphabetical Order

B. Use the lines below to write the spelling words in alphabetical order.

1. _____   6. _____   11. _____   16. _____
2. _____   7. _____   12. _____   17. _____
3. _____   8. _____   13. _____   18. _____
4. _____   9. _____   14. _____   19. _____
5. _____   10. _____   15. _____   20. _____

LC 1.5 Spell roots, suffixes, prefixes, contractions, and syllable
constructions correctly.

Name _____

Proofreading

A. Circle the misspelled words in the passage. Write the words correctly on the lines below.

Ana Rosa climbed up the gri gri tree in order to concentrayt. It was a perfect locasion for watching the ocean. One day, Ana Rosa saw something that broke her consentrasion: a sea monster! At first no one believed her, but then it turned out that she was correcte. People met to diskus the sea monster. Their discusion lasted late into the night.

1. _____   3. _____   5. _____

2. _____   4. _____   6. _____

B. Writing Activity

Write a paragraph about a time when you or a person you know planned an event or an activity. Use four words from your spelling list.

_____

_____

_____

_____

_____

_____

_____

_____

_____

_____

_____

_____

 LC 1.5 Spell roots, suffixes, prefixes, contractions, and syllable constructions correctly.

Name _____

• In **comparisons**, the adjective *bad* has an irregular form. *Worse* and *worst* are the irregular forms of *bad*.
• Use *worse* to compare two people, places, or things.
• Use *worst* to compare more than two.

Rewrite each sentence, correcting the form of *bad* where necessary.

1. Winter is the worse time to visit the República Dominicana.

   _____

   _____

2. Making a fuss about the sea monster would be worst than not telling anybody.

   _____

   _____

3. Guario thinks that sitting in a gri gri tree is the worser way to spend time.

   _____

   _____

4. Roberto complained that washing dishes was a worst chore than sweeping.

   _____

   _____

5. Spring is a worst time than winter for whales to migrate.

   _____

6. Spotting the sea monster was not the worse thing that happened that day.

   _____

   _____

7. Roberto was a worser domino player than Papi.

   _____

8. Ana Rosa had a worst time at the gathering than her neighbors.

   _____

   _____

Name _____

Read the paragraph below. Rewrite the paragraph correctly on the lines provided.

Once, far beneath the sailboats that float on the sea, lived the most best swimmer in the ocean. He could swim faster than the fastest dolphin, and no fish was gooder at diving deep, deep down. This fine swimmer was also the biggest creature in all the sea, and he scared away the baby fish. The worstest thing about his size was that the other ocean creatures called him a sea monster, and no one wanted to be his friend. He thought there was nothing worser than being so big.

_____

_____

_____

_____

_____

_____

_____

_____

_____

_____

_____

_____

_____

_____

LC 1.0 Written and Oral English Language Conventions

© Macmillan/McGraw-Hill

Name _____

Read:

The cafeteria food at our school is terrible. For example…

Think about ONE specific cafeteria meal that was terrible.

Write three sentences to add to the sentence above. Use sensory details.

Example: *The cafeteria food at our school is terrible. Last week, five people complained to the cafeteria manager because the pizza was burnt.*

The cafeteria food at our school is terrible…

_____

_____

_____

_____

_____

_____

_____

_____

_____

_____

_____

_____

_____

_____

Many words have their origin in the Greek language. Word roots are word parts that usually can't stand on their own. Knowing the meanings of **Greek roots** can help you define unfamiliar words.

Read the chart. Then write a word from the box below to correctly complete each sentence.

Greek root	Meaning	Example
astr	star	astronaut
auto	self, same	automatic
photo	light	photogenic
mech	machine	mechanism
graph	thing written	graphic
phon	sound, voice	phonetic

photocopy   astronomer   automobile
biography   mechanic   phonics

1. The vehicle needed a _____ who knew how its engine worked.

2. We studied sounds and syllables in our _____ class.

3. Ms. Brown made one more _____ of the worksheet for the new student.

4. The author wrote a _____ about Harriet Tubman.

5. Thanks to the _____, we don't have to walk to school.

6. An _____ looked at the stars through her telescope.

© Macmillan/McGraw-Hill

 R 1.0 Word Analysis, Fluency, and Systematic Vocabulary Development

Name _____

A. Select the best word from the choices in parentheses. Then write the correct word on the line provided.

1. Have you seen the (categories, corners) of talents that will be allowed at the talent contest? _____

2. Did you see the size of the stage? It's (slow, gigantic)! _____

3. We walked to the contest in the rain, and now our clothes are (soggy, dry).

   _____

4. The man was tired, so he (slumped, sat up) in his chair and went to sleep.

   _____

5. Cynthia twisted (blocks, strands) of hair around her finger.

   _____

6. If we write a paper, will Mr. Price give us extra (credit, time)?

   _____

7. Our school has lights in front of the stage, so all of the performers have a (luminous, dark) glow on their faces. _____

8. All of the performers were quite (splendid, capable) of putting on a good show. _____

B. Write new sentences for two of the vocabulary words used above. Then underline the vocabulary word.

9. _____

   _____

10. _____

    _____

The **characters** are the people or animals in a story. The **plot** is a series of events that take the characters through an experience or change. In some stories, the plot includes a problem that a character has to solve.

Read the passage and answer the questions below.

Tuesday, I caught a bad cold and had to stay home from school. The next day was Wednesday, and Mrs. Mandle always assigned an essay that day. That afternoon I called my best friend, Roberto. He is a great writer and listens carefully to Mrs. Mandle's essay questions. However, when I called Roberto, his voice was muffled and what he said wasn't very clear.

"Mike," Roberto said, "the essay is on 'what makes blueberry pies.'"

"What?" I said. "The essay is on 'what makes blueberry pies'?"

"Yes," he said. "I hope you feel butter. I have to go to digger now."

That night I wrote about blueberry pies and how to make them. The next day I felt better and went to school. I saw Roberto and talked about my blueberry pie essay.

"Blueberry pies?" Roberto asked. "We didn't have to write about blueberry pies. Our essay was about 'what makes blue skies.'"

1. Who are the characters in this passage? _____

_____

2. What is Mike's main problem? _____

_____

3. Why does Mike call Roberto for the essay question? _____

_____

_____

4. What could Mike have done differently to solve his essay problem?

_____

_____

R 2.0 Reading Comprehension (Focus on Informational Materials)

Name _____

As you read *Miss Alaineus*, fill in the Character and Plot Chart.

Character	Plot

How does the information you wrote in this Character and Plot Chart help you analyze the story structure of *Miss Alaineus*?

As I read, I will pay attention to intonation and phrasing.

	Freddy slapped the table as he snorted. "Check this out,
10	Eva!" he said between chuckles.
15	Freddy grabbed my sketchbook and held it up next to my
26	startled face. Eva frowned, looked confused, and then finally
35	a gigantic smile crossed her face.
41	"You're good, Nadia," she said. "But I don't get it."
51	What I'd drawn was a cartoon of *me*, with an oversized
62	head and tiny body. I'd added my trademark features.
71	A banner at the top read "Science UN-Fair." Question marks
81	spun around my head, and I had a very confused look—a
93	perfect caricature, I might add.
98	Freddy turned to me and said, "Eva was in the nurse's
109	office during fifth period. Remember? She got hurt playing
118	soccer during lunch."
121	"Oh, yeah," I said. And then I told Eva what she had
133	missed. 134

Comprehension Check

1. Who is the main character of this story? **Character**

2. What did Nadia draw in her sketchbook? **Plot Development**

	Words Read	−	Number of Errors	=	Words Correct Score
First Read		−		=	
Second Read		−		=	

R 1.1 Read aloud narrative and expository text fluently and accurately and with appropriate pacing, **intonation**, and expression.

© Macmillan/McGraw-Hill

Name _____

> **Photographs** or drawings provide a visual image of what
> is happening in the story. **Captions** help explain what the
> photographs or drawings are about.

**Look at the drawing and read the caption. Then answer the
questions.**

Fifth-graders learn about fitness and health by running a one-mile race.

1. What does the drawing show? _____

_____

_____

2. What other information do you learn from the caption? _____

_____

_____

 R 2.1 Understand how text features (e.g., format, graphics,
sequence, diagrams, illustrations, charts, maps) make information
accessible and usable.

You can learn the meaning of an unfamiliar word by using the words around it as clues. Look at the words that appear near the word that you don't know, and try to find a **synonym** of that word to help you figure out its meaning. Remember that a synonym is a word with a similar meaning.

Circle the synonym of the underlined word in each sentence.

1. The size of the hot-air balloon <u>decreased</u> and diminished as air was let out of it.

2. The awful sound was <u>unbearable</u> and it woke me up.

3. The roses <u>flourished</u> and thrived more than any other plant in Mrs. Lyon's garden.

4. It can be <u>hazardous</u> to play near a downed power line because electric currents are dangerous.

5. Chris was modest about winning his national award because he is <u>humble</u>.

6. The <u>extravagant</u> party had circus performers, an orchestra, and chefs. Bob thought it was too expensive for only a few guests.

7. The letter was <u>anonymous</u>, so the sender is unknown.

8. The basketball team returned <u>victorious</u> because they had won the state championship.

9. The teachers said soda is <u>prohibited</u> because bottles are forbidden in the gym.

10. The paper towel will soak up the spilled milk because it will <u>absorb</u> all the moisture.

© Macmillan/McGraw-Hill

 R 1.3 Understand and explain frequently used synonyms, antonyms, and homographs.

Name _____

Using the Word Study Steps

1. LOOK at the word.
2. SAY the word aloud.
3. STUDY the letters in the word.

4. WRITE the word.
5. CHECK the word.
   Did you spell the word right?
   If not, go back to step 1.

A. Fill-Ins

Fill in the missing letters of each word to form a spelling word.

1. a ____ t ____ onaut
2. a ____ t ____ graph
3. aut ____ m ____ tic
4. a ____ to ____ ____ bile
5. m ____ ____ hical
6. ____ e ____ egraph
7. t ____ l ____ phone
8. ____ el ____ ____ cope
9. te ____ ____ ____ ision
10. te ____ eg ____ am

11. hom ____ ____ h ____ ne
12. p ____ o ____ ics
13. di ____ a ____ ____ er
14. ____ st ____ ____ nomer
15. p ____ ____ t ____ graph
16. ____ ____ otogr ____ phy
17. m ____ ____ h
18. me ____ ____ an ____ c
19. ____ ec ____ anic ____ l
20. t ____ le ____ ____ oto

B. Make a Puzzle

Make up a puzzle of your own using the space on this page. Give it to someone else to solve. Be sure to include at least five spelling words in your puzzle.

 LC 1.5 Spell roots, suffixes, prefixes, contractions, and syllable
constructions correctly.

Name _____

**A. Circle the misspelled words in the passage. Write the words
correctly on the lines below.**

Andrea turned on the telivision. There was a program on about a
mithical bird and a horse. She picked up the telefone to call Jill, but
no one answered. The automatick answering machine clicked on, and
Andrea began to leave a message.

"I was doing my phonicks homework when this show came on!"
she exclaimed. "There's a bird on TV that looks just like the one in the
photagraph you have. Turn on channel eight, if you're home."

1. _____ 2. _____ 3. _____

4. _____ 5. _____ 6. _____

B. Writing Activity

**Write a paragraph about what you would have done if you were
Sage. Use four words from your spelling list.**

_____

_____

_____

_____

_____

_____

_____

_____

_____

_____

_____

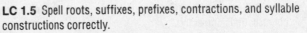

CA **LC 1.5** Spell roots, suffixes, prefixes, contractions, and syllable
constructions correctly.

© Macmillan/McGraw-Hill

Name _____

An **adverb** can describe a verb. It can also describe an adjective or another adverb.

A. In these sentences, the adverbs describe verbs, adverbs, or adjectives. Underline each adverb. Some sentences contain more than one adverb.

1. The Golden Mare spoke quietly.

2. Yelena the Fair realized that she would be in danger very soon.

3. The Tsar was terribly angry about Alexi's success.

4. The Lake of the Sun shone brilliantly in the morning.

5. The Water of Youth began to boil very quickly.

B. Complete each sentence with an adverb that describes the underlined word. Choose from the adverbs in the box.

almost	very	completely	finally	quite	rather	too

6. The Tsar acted _____ greedily.

7. They poured water into the iron pot until it was _____ full.

8. The ship moved _____ gracefully across the water.

9. Alexi stayed awake _____ late that night.

10. Alexi and the Golden Mare _____ defeated the Tsar.

© Macmillan/McGraw-Hill

Name _____

Read the paragraph below. Rewrite the paragraph correctly on the lines provided.

The Golden Mare was real old when she met Alexi. Because she was amazing, she looked and felt quitely healthy and young. The Golden Mare could gallop quick through the forest as though she were made of wind. Her hooves hard hit the ground when she ran. Alexi could not believe his well fortune when he saw this mysterious creature. He rough rubbed his eyes, expecting the horse to disappear sudden.

_____

_____

_____

_____

_____

_____

_____

_____

_____

_____

_____

_____

_____

_____

_____

© Macmillan/McGraw-Hill

Name _____

1. Remember that there are many ways to vary sentences. Here are two that we have discussed:

   • Change the verb.

   • Include dialogue.

2. Read the following sentence:

   Franklin wanted to do well on the quiz, so he made sure to study for several hours.

3. List three other ways to say "want."

   a. (**example**: desire)

   b.

   c.

4. List three other ways to say "study."

   a. (**example**: review)

   b.

   c.

5. Rewrite the sentence. Change the verb:

   Example: Franklin wanted to do well on the quiz, so he remembered to review for several hours.

6. Rewrite the sentence. Include dialogue:

   Example: "Mom," Franklin whined, "I can't clean my room right now. You know I've got this quiz. I'm going to fail if I don't study for it!"

7. Read the following sentence:

   Even though dogs are more common as pets, pigs are actually more intelligent.

8. Rewrite the sentence two times using two ways to vary sentences.

CA **W 1.0** Writing Strategies

Many words in English have **Latin roots**. You can define unfamiliar words by recognizing a Latin root and using context clues.

Latin Roots	Meaning
aud	to hear
tract	to drag, draw
port	to carry
spect	to look
mit/miss	to send

Read the root chart, and write the root of each underlined word in the sentences below. Then use context clues and the meaning of the Latin roots to write a definition of each underlined word.

1. Making a campfire is tricky. First, an adult must <u>transport</u> wood

   to your campsite. _____ **Transport** means _____.

2. Then you must <u>inspect</u> the wood to make sure that it is dry. _____

   Inspect means _____.

3. When an adult lights the fire, you will notice an <u>audible</u> *crackle* and *pop* as

   the wood begins to burn. _____ **Audible** means _____

   _____.

4. The <u>spectacle</u> of a roaring fire is a wonderful sight. _____

   Spectacle means _____.

5. For some people, the main <u>attraction</u> of a campfire is roasting

   marshmallows. _____ **Attraction** means _____

   _____.

 R 1.0 Word Analysis, Fluency, and Systematic Vocabulary Development

A. In the sentences below, circle *correct* if the boldface vocabulary word is used properly. If it is not used correctly, circle *incorrect*.

1. The boring television show was **arousing** the children's interest.

   correct　　　　**incorrect**

2. The baby deer that was **nestled** in the grass looked peaceful.

   correct　　　　**incorrect**

3. The **secluded** spot was ideal for a picnic because it was out in the open where everyone could see it.

   correct　　　　**incorrect**

4. The many streams high in the mountains are the **source** of **the** river that flows in the valley below.

   correct　　　　**incorrect**

5. The **unpleasant** encounter with the skunk is one of Carlos's unhappiest memories.

   correct　　　　**incorrect**

6. The **behavior** of the animal's fur helps it blend in with its surroundings.

   correct　　　　**incorrect**

B. Write a sentence for each vocabulary word below.

7. stunned _____

   _____

8. glimpse _____

   _____

Authors have a purpose, or reason, for writing. An **author's purpose** might be to persuade, to inform, to explain, or to entertain.

Read each passage below. On the lines provided, write whether the author's main purpose is to persuade, to inform, to explain, or to entertain. Then write a sentence to explain your answer.

1. If you're thinking of finding a new hobby, then you should seriously consider bird-watching. First of all, it involves spending time outdoors. Many trips are planned with groups of people, so bird-watching is a good way to make new friends. Best of all, you get to see many interesting birds. Pick up your binoculars today!

   Author's purpose: _____ _____

   _____

   _____

2. I frantically called to my dog Frisky, but it was already too late. She had spotted the skunk and was running after it happily. Frisky just wanted to play, but the skunk didn't know that. As the skunk lifted its tail, Frisky leaned down to get a sniff, and the skunk sprayed her right in the face. Poor Frisky! And poor me! I had to give her a bath.

   Author's purpose: _____

   _____

   _____

3. A skunk is a small, furry animal with black and white markings. Skunks are part of the weasel family. They are best known for the highly offensive liquid that they spray when they are frightened. This smelly liquid is called musk. A skunk can spray its musk as far as ten feet.

   Author's purpose: _____

   _____

   _____

 R 2.0 Reading Comprehension (Focus on Informational Materials)

As you read *Carlos and the Skunk*, fill in the Author's Purpose Chart.

Clues	Author's Purpose

How does the information you wrote in the Author's Purpose Chart help you evaluate *Carlos and the Skunk*?

As I read, I will pay attention to intonation.

Lizards, turtles, and snakes are all reptiles. They live in
10 | a world full of danger. Predators are on the prowl, looking
21 | to eat reptiles that aren't careful. Animals may try to steal
32 | their territory or their eggs, or eat them. Reptiles aren't
42 | helpless, though. They have many defenses they can use to
52 | protect themselves and their homes.
57 | In the face of a threat, a reptile's usual behavior is to avoid
70 | it. Lizards dart away. Snakes slither away. Turtles hide in
80 | their shells or slip into the water. Escape is sometimes the
91 | only way to live another day. Often, though, staying out of
102 | trouble isn't possible. That's when a reptile uses its defenses
112 | to help it stay alive. It may use color, size, special body parts,
125 | or even deadly poison to survive. Read on to learn more.
136 | Sometimes a reptile can't run away from danger. Most
145 | will then try to scare the predator away. Some change the
156 | way they stand. Others change the way they look. 165

Comprehension Check

1. What is the main idea of this passage? **Main Idea and Details**

2. What special defenses may reptiles use? **Main Idea and Details**

	Words Read	−	Number of Errors	=	Words Correct Score
First Read		−		=	
Second Read		−		=	

© Macmillan/McGraw-Hill

R 1.1 Read aloud narrative and expository text fluently and accurately
and with appropriate pacing, **intonation**, and expression.

A **deck** is a short preview of a magazine article that is designed to grab the reader's attention. **Headings** are subtitles that break an article into different parts. They help readers organize information so it is easier to understand.

Read the magazine article that follows. Then answer the questions.

Animal Self-Defense
by Elle Wainwright

If you were a wild animal about to become someone's dinner, what would you do? Run? Hide? Fight? Animals may do any of these things when they feel threatened.

Hide and Seek

Some adaptations help animals hide. An animal can seem to disappear by using camouflage.

1. What is the title of the article? _____
_____

2. What is the byline? _____
_____

3. What is the deck? _____
_____
_____
_____

4. What is the heading? _____
_____

Name _____

You can define an unknown word by using **context clues**, the words around an unknown word that give you clues to the word's meaning.

Circle the context clues in each sentence that can help you figure out the meaning of the underlined word. Then write the definition of the underlined word on the line.

1. The skunk, <u>unaware</u> how bad Tina smelled after spraying her, walked away as if nothing happened.

   unaware: _____

2. The hiker was a <u>coward</u> and was frightened at even the smallest sound.

   coward: _____

3. The <u>location</u> of the town was unknown, but Tom believed he knew where the place was.

   location: _____

4. The boat had a tough time <u>navigating</u> the rough seas, but the dolphins had no problem making their way through the waves.

   navigating: _____

5. The thornbug's camouflage was <u>flawless</u>, and the students marveled at its perfect disguise.

   flawless: _____

6. He was so <u>grouchy</u> after being sprayed by the skunk that nothing could change his grumpy mood.

   grouchy: _____

7. The <u>pesky</u> mosquito annoyed the girl as it buzzed in her ear.

   pesky: _____

8. The cliffs marked the southern <u>boundary</u> of the village, and the river marked the northern edge.

   boundary: _____

© Macmillan/McGraw-Hill

CA **R 1.0** Word Analysis, Fluency, and Systematic Vocabulary Development

Name _____

Using the Word Study Steps

1. LOOK at the word.

2. SAY the word aloud.

3. STUDY the letters in the word.

4. WRITE the word.

5. CHECK the word.
Did you spell the word right?
If not, go back to step 1.

A. Find and Circle

Find and circle each of the spelling words in this puzzle. Words may read forward, backward, upward, or downward.

```
E R E S P E C T S S I M S I D O A A S R
L V T R A N S P O R T I M P O R T T P O
I H S N O I T A T R O P S N A R T T E T
S W M C N E E E T T I M M O C N Z R C C
S N O I S S I M R E T N I T Y F F A T E
I I P D I S T R A C T E X P O R T C A P
M T P O R T A B L E T C E P S U S T T S
E L C A T C E P S T C E P S N I M I O N
N O I S S I M R J T R A C T O R J O R I
N O I T C A R T B U S G N Q M P R N Z O
```

B. List the words below as you find them in the puzzle.

1. _____   8. _____   15. _____

2. _____   9. _____   16. _____

3. _____   10. _____   17. _____

4. _____   11. _____   18. _____

5. _____   12. _____   19. _____

6. _____   13. _____   20. _____

7. _____   14. _____

LC 1.5 Spell roots, suffixes, prefixes, contractions, and syllable constructions correctly.

Carlos and the Skunk
Grade 5/Unit 6   **333**

Name _____

A. Circle the misspelled words in the passage. Write the words correctly on the lines below.

My uncle and I went camping for three days. Our car broke down on the first day, so we lost our means of transportasion. My uncle could only inspekt our car—he couldn't fix it. We found an abandoned tracktor on the second day, but that didn't work, either. Luckily, I had brought my portabel radio with me, so we called for help on the third day. The town put together a comittee and went on a mision to save us.

1. _____   2. _____   3. _____

4. _____   5. _____   6. _____

B. Writing Activity

Write a paragraph about why you would or would not like to go camping. Use four words from your spelling list.

_____

_____

_____

_____

_____

_____

_____

_____

_____

_____

© Macmillan/McGraw-Hill

 LC 1.5 Spell roots, suffixes, prefixes, contractions, and syllable constructions correctly.

Name _____

- Use *more* or *most* to form comparisons with adverbs that end in -*ly* and with most other adverbs having two or more syllables.
- Use *more* to compare two actions; use *most* to compare more than two.
- When you use *more* or *most*, do not use the ending -*er* or -*est*.

A. Read the sentences. Write the correct form of the adverb in parentheses.

1. (hungrily) Of them all, it was Teddy who stared at the hot dogs _____.

2. (patiently) Bobby waited _____ than Teddy did.

3. (quietly) Bobby worked _____ of them all.

4. (quickly) Teddy walked _____ than Bobby did.

5. (easily) Uncle Curtis got lost _____ than Teddy did.

B. Read each sentence. If the adverb is correct, write *Correct* on the line. If it is not correct, rewrite the sentence with the correct form of the adverb.

6. Uncle Curtis grinned happiliest of all.

_____

7. Bobby learned more quicklier than Teddy.

_____

8. Uncle Curtis ate slowlier than the boys.

_____

9. Teddy treated the map more carefully than did Uncle Curtis.

_____

10. Teddy eats more noisily of all.

_____

© Macmillan/McGraw-Hill

Name _____

**Read the letter below. Rewrite the letter correctly on the lines
provided.**

Dear Mom and Dad,

    I know you think that I'm messy, but I clean more carefullier than
Mother Nature does. There are dirt and rocks everywhere in the woods!
Since we've been at the campsite, we've been eating most poorly than we
do at home. You cook much more expert than Uncle Curtis does. Of all
the campers, it's the mosquitoes who seem to be eating happiliest. I hope
we come home more sooner rather than late.

                       Your son,

                       Teddy

_____

_____

_____

_____

_____

_____

_____

_____

_____

_____

_____

_____

CA LC 1.0 Written and Oral English Language Conventions

Name _____

1. Read the following passage:

   Poodles are playful and fun. Poodles are really cute. Poodles are also probably one of the best pets to have in general because they are fun and they aren't messy. More importantly, I have never heard of a poodle hurting a human or another dog. Poodles are just gentle and nice.

2. Notice that four out of five sentences begin with the word "poodles."

3. Remember that sometimes repeating a word gives a sense of rhythm to a piece of writing.

4. Note, though, that in this case, the sentences sound like they are repeating the same thing over and over.

5. Remember that when you are combining sentences, you are just trying to do it differently. AFTER you write it differently, THEN you can decide if you like it better. Most of the time, you'll need to try a bunch of different ways of combining before you find something you like better than the original.

6. Try combining the first two sentences (this is easy!):

   Poodles are playful and fun. Poodles are really cute.

   (Example: Poodles are really cute because they are playful and fun.)

7. Try combining these sentences (this is harder!):

   Poodles are really cute. More importantly, I have never heard of a poodle hurting a human or another dog.

   (Example: I think poodles are really cute, and it is not just because I have never heard of a poodle hurting a human or another dog.)

8. Turn to your journal entry and choose two sentences that you will try to combine: (They don't have to be two sentences that follow one another.)

   Sentence 1:

   Sentence 2:

The origins of many English words are the names of characters from Greek and Roman mythology. Recognizing **words from mythology** can help you figure out the meanings of some unfamiliar words.

A. Match each word to the name from Greek or Roman mythology that best explains each word's origin. Then write the letter of the name on the line.

1. fortune _____

2. cosmic _____

3. titanic _____

4. volcano _____

5. cereal _____

6. jovial _____

7. geology _____

8. furious _____

9. January _____

10. Olympics _____

a. Jove, the Roman god who controlled the weather

b. Fortuna, the Roman goddess of luck

c. Gaea, the Greek Earth goddess

d. Furies, angry spirits in Greek mythology

e. Janus, the Roman god of beginnings

f. Cosmos, the Greek word for *universe*

g. Mount Olympus, the home of the gods in Greek mythology

h. Titans, Greek giants who had enormous strength

i. Ceres, the Roman goddess of grain

j. Vulcan, the Roman god of fire

B. Use four words from the first column to make two sentences.

11. _____

_____

12. _____

_____

© Macmillan/McGraw-Hill

CA R 1.0 Word Analysis, Fluency, and Systematic Vocabulary Development

Name _____

A. Match the words with their definitions. Then write the letter on the line.

1. rigid _____   a. of or relating to the body

2. wheelchair _____   b. not yielding or bending

3. interact _____   c. simple or basic

4. physical _____   d. a chair mounted on wheels

5. elementary _____   e. to act on or influence each other

B. Choose the word in parentheses that will complete each sentence. Then write the word on the line.

6. Children should learn (physical, rigid) activities that they will still enjoy when they are adults. _____

7. Sports that allow you to (salute, interact) with the natural environment are exciting. _____

8. The team followed a (rigid, gracious) exercise routine that involved running a mile, doing 100 push-ups, and jumping rope every day.

   _____

9. A person in a (parasol, wheelchair) can compete in the Paralympics.

   _____

10. Pete was new to sailing, so he took an (elementary, diverse) sailing class to learn more. _____

C. Find the vocabulary words in the word search below.

11. j u w o i c s p h y s i c a l l k j

12. a k j e l e m e n t a r y u e u y p

13. r i g y i u o w h e e l c h a i r z

14. a r l r i g i d l k j j f i n t e r

R 1.0 Word Analysis, Fluency, and Systematic Vocabulary Development

You encounter techniques of **persuasion** every day. Persuasion is communication meant to convince you that you should believe something, act in a certain way, or participate in something. People trying to persuade you can use a variety of techniques.

Techniques of Persuasion
Testimonial: A noteworthy person supports a product.
Bandwagon: The product or activity is said to be popular with everyone.
Emotional appeal: Language is used to make a person feel strong emotions.
Repetition: A product or service name is repeated many times.
Slogan: A catchy phrase is used to sell a product.

Match a technique of persuasion to each example.

1. Our wheelchairs are used nationwide by all Paralympians everywhere.

   _____

2. Boundless Playgrounds are fun! Boundless Playgrounds are safe!

   Boundless Playgrounds make memories! _____

3. A GPS device in your hands makes your feet "Glad to Walk Positively

   Anywhere Safely." _____

4. Hi, I'm proud to use FastBreak Wheelchairs. Because of FastBreak Wheelchairs, I was named one of the top young athletes in the nation.

   _____

5. Would you enjoy never going anywhere new, never hearing new sounds, and never meeting new people? Probably not. With GPS, you can be free to walk anywhere, any way, and any time that you want!

   _____

© Macmillan/McGraw-Hill

CA R 2.0 Reading Comprehension (Focus on Informational Materials)

Name _____

As you read "A Dream Comes True," fill in the Fact and Opinion Chart.

Fact	Opinion

How does the information you wrote in this Fact and Opinion Chart help
you monitor comprehension of "A Dream Comes True"?

As I read, I will pay attention to pronunciation.

	Wheelchair basketball is probably the oldest competitive
7	wheelchair sport. It began after World War II as a way to get
19	disabled veterans active. Now children ages six and up are
29	playing wheelchair basketball in gyms everywhere. They
36	play on the same size court and use most of the same rules as
50	their classmates. And they're getting a lot of exercise, too.
60	Only a few rules are adapted in wheelchair basketball.
69	For example, if a player takes more than two pushes of the
81	wheelchair while dribbling, a traveling penalty is called. Even
90	if only the wheel of a player's wheelchair goes out of bounds,
102	the player is out of bounds. A player who lifts out of his or her
117	seat to get a **physical** advantage gets charged with a foul. So
129	does a player whose feet touch the floor.
137	Like wheelchair hockey, each wheelchair basketball player
144	is classified according to his or her ability level.
153	Wheelchair basketball, like wheelchair hockey, takes
159	coordination. Players must use their hands to move their
168	wheelchairs. At the same time, they must be able to handle
179	the ball. 181

Comprehension Check

1. Why does wheelchair basketball take coordination? **Main Idea and Details**

2. Why are sports adapted for wheelchairs? **Cause and Effect**

	Words Read	–	Number of Errors	=	Words Correct Score
First Read		–		=	
Second Read		–		=	

 R 1.1 Read aloud narrative and expository text fluently and accurately and with appropriate pacing, intonation, and expression.

Name _____

You see printed materials that provide information about the world around you every day. **Everyday communications** have many forms.

Study the descriptions below. Then answer the questions.

Consumer materials	Warranty: guarantees a product or its parts for a period of time
	Product instructions: explain how to operate a product
Directions	Maps explain how to get from one place to another.
Advertisements	Help-wanted ad: explains a particular job and how to apply for it
	Store ad: provides information about the store and its merchandise
Brochure	a small booklet that contains information about a place, service, person, or object
Newsletter	a printed report or letter giving information about a special group or organization

1. What might you read if you were looking for a job? _____

2. Would you read a brochure or a warranty to learn more about a museum

   exhibit? _____

3. A neighborhood club is planning a Fourth of July parade. What would you

   read to find out when and where the parade begins? _____

4. What might you read to learn how to operate your new camera?

   _____

5. What would you use to get directions from California to Texas?

   _____

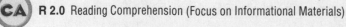

R 2.0 Reading Comprehension (Focus on Informational Materials)

Name _____

Problem/Solution Writing Frame

A. Summarize "A Dream Comes True." Use the Problem/Solution Writing Frame below.

Hannah Kristan, like other children in wheelchairs, is unable to play on most playground equipment.

To **solve** this **problem**, Boundless Playgrounds _____

_____

_____

_____

_____.

As a result, _____

_____

_____

_____.

To get a special playground in her town, Hannah _____

_____

_____

_____.

As a result, children with disabilities can now enjoy playing with children of all abilities.

B. Rewrite the completed summary on another sheet of paper. Keep it as a model for writing a summary of an article or selection using this text structure.

 R 2.0 Reading Comprehension

© Macmillan/McGraw-Hill

You can figure out the meaning of an unfamiliar word by using **context clues**, the words around the unfamiliar word.

Read each sentence. Use context clues to help you define the boldface word. Then write the letter of the best choice on the line.

1. During the game, my **opponent** was the best player on the other team.

   An opponent is _____ .

   a. a competitor   **b.** an ally   **c.** a coach

2. The athletes trained at a high **altitude** because it is much more difficult to run in the mountains.

   Altitude is _____ .

   a. an underwater cave   **b.** the height above sea level   **c.** a plateau

3. The winning women's basketball team looked **regal** with their gold medals and flowers on top of the podium.

   Regal means _____ .

   a. deprived of food   **b.** serious   **c.** like royalty

4. Joe was accompanied by his guide dog, who **escorted** him into the gymnasium.

   To be escorted is to be _____ .

   a. complex   **b.** guided   **c.** called

5. For months the team practiced their **maneuvers**, until the exercises became natural to them.

   Maneuvers are _____ .

   a. movements   **b.** schedules   **c.** relationships

Name _____

Using the Word Study Steps

1. LOOK at the word.

2. SAY the word aloud.

3. STUDY the letters in the word.

4. WRITE the word.

5. CHECK the word.
   Did you spell the word right?
   If not, go back to step 1.

A. Fill-Ins

Fill in the missing letters of each word to form a spelling word.

1. c ___ re ___ l

2. te ___ ra ___ e

3. gr ___ ___ ious

4. e ___ ___ o

5. gi ___ an ___ ic

6. o ___ e ___ n

7. at ___ ___ s

8. cl ___ t ___ es

9. ter ___ i ___ ory

10. p ___ ra ___ ol

11. mo ___ ___ al

12. f ___ ___ y

13. f ___ ___ ious

14. J ___ n ___ ___ ry

15. O ___ ___ mp ___ cs

16. s ___ lu ___ e

17. c ___ ___ le

18. cy ___ lo ___ e

19. l ___ n ___ r

20. for ___ ___ ___ e

B. Use the spelling words above to help you write a poem of at least four lines.

_____

_____

_____

_____

© Macmillan/McGraw-Hill

 LC 1.5 Spell roots, suffixes, prefixes, contractions, and syllable constructions correctly.

A. Circle the misspelled words in the passage. Write the words correctly on the lines below.

Jake heard his footsteps ecko as he walked into the jigantic stadium. Today he would compete in his first Olimpics. He had been training since Janyuary. He swam in the osean three times a week and had been watching his diet closely. This morning he had eaten a bowl of sereal and a piece of toast. The day he had been waiting for had finally come.

1. _____ 2. _____ 3. _____

4. _____ 5. _____ 6. _____

B. Writing Activity

Write a paragraph about a time when you helped someone accomplish a goal. Use four words from your spelling list.

_____

_____

_____

_____

_____

_____

_____

_____

_____

_____

_____

CA LC 1.5 Spell roots, suffixes, prefixes, contractions, and syllable constructions correctly.

A Dream Comes True
Grade 5/Unit 6   **347**

Name _____

Correct a sentence with two negatives by changing one negative word to a positive word.

Negative	Positive
no, none	any
never	ever
nothing	anything
nobody	anybody
no one	anyone
nowhere	anywhere

Rewrite each sentence, replacing one of the negative words with a positive word.

1. The kids never have nothing bad to say about gym class.

   _____

   _____

2. No one never passes up a chance to learn kickboxing.

   _____

   _____

3. No person nowhere should be without a new GPS device.

   _____

   _____

4. What if you couldn't find nobody to give you directions?

   _____

   _____

5. None of the athletes says nothing negative.

   _____

6. There weren't no playgrounds where she could play.

   _____

 CA LC 1.0 Written and Oral English Language Conventions

Practice

Grammar:
Negatives

Name _____

Read the paragraph below. Rewrite the paragraph correctly on the lines provided.

Thank you, Sara, and good morning, everyone. There aren't no boring sports headlines today! First, the Paralympics began last night. None of the athletes had no trouble showing spirit. The fans, too, never showed nothing but excitement. During the first basketball game, nobody couldn't get no shot past Jennifer Howitt. She didn't defend the basket with no fancy moves—she just played well. Her team had never won no games before last night. They couldn't not be more proud. The players on the other team weren't never sorry that they lost. These Paralympic athletes are not never sore losers. The positive energy at the game was thrilling! And now back to you, Sara, for the day's weather.

_____
_____
_____
_____
_____
_____
_____
_____
_____
_____
_____
_____

CA **LC 1.0** Written and Oral English Language Conventions

A Dream Comes True **349**
Grade 5/Unit 6

Name _____

Writing Rubric

4 Excellent	3 Good	2 Fair	1 Unsatisfactory
Ideas and Content/Genre	Ideas and Content/Genre	Ideas and Content/Genre	Ideas and Content/Genre
Organization and Focus	Organization and Focus	Organization and Focus	Organization and Focus
Sentence Structure/Fluency	Sentence Structure/Fluency	Sentence Structure/Fluency	Sentence Structure/Fluency
Conventions	Conventions	Conventions	Conventions
Word Choice	Word Choice	Word Choice	Word Choice
Voice	Voice	Voice	Voice
Presentation	Presentation	Presentation	Presentation

© Macmillan/McGraw-Hill

Name _____

A prefix is a word part that can be added to the beginning of other words or word parts to change the word's meaning. Some prefixes refer to an amount and are called **number prefixes**.

Prefix	Number	Example
uni-	1	unity
bi-	2	bicycle
tri-	3	triceratops
cent-	100	centennial

A. Choose the best prefix for the boldface word. Then write the complete word on the line.

1. The girl put on her soccer _____**form** before the game.

   _____

2. Every _____**meter** counts when carefully measuring the length of

   a board. _____

3. The _____**cycle** has three wheels. _____

4. Stephanie was _____**lingual** and knew two languages.

   _____

B. Circle the prefix in each word. Then write a definition of the word that is based on the meaning of the prefix.

5. triangle _____

6. universe _____

7. bisect _____

8. centipede _____

9. tripod _____

10. unicorn _____

© Macmillan/McGraw-Hill

Name _____

founding	civilization	shortage	outcast
traditional	strategy	complex	reflected

A. Choose words from the box to complete the sentences below.

1. When fall came, there was no _____ of fruit from the large orchard.

2. The shiny leaves _____ the bright light of the afternoon sun.

3. In history class, we are studying the _____ of our town back in the 1800s.

4. Breeding hybrid fruits and vegetables is _____ work, but eating them is simple.

5. The teacher taught his students to always include everyone and not to

   make anyone feel like an _____.

6. Dusting the plants with flour was part of their _____ to protect the tomato plants from insects.

7. Our _____ holiday dessert is apple pie.

8. Our _____ has a long history of growing grain to feed people and trading the extra grain for other goods.

B. Possible definitions of the vocabulary words are below. Circle whether the given definition is true or false.

9. T F strategy: a careful plan

10. T F outcast: a well-liked individual

11. T F shortage: an abundance or a large amount

12. T F complex: hard to understand or do

CA R 1.0 Word Analysis, Fluency, and Systematic Vocabulary Development

Name _____

> The essential message, or **theme**, of a story, is the overall idea or message about life that the author wants to give readers. To find the theme, think about what happens as a result of the characters' words and actions. This will help you to figure out what the author thinks is meaningful and important.

Read the passage. Then answer the questions.

Wesley often found new ways of doing things that he liked better than the ordinary ways.

Some of Wesley's ideas helped him prove himself to the other children in the neighborhood. Before Wesley founded Weslandia, the children in the neighborhood had teased him because they did not understand him. Instead of fitting in by imitating the others, Wesley made friends by being himself.

1. Why did the other children tease Wesley? _____

_____

_____

2. Do you think the author believes that imitating other people to get along is a good idea? Explain your answer.

_____

_____

_____

3. Do you agree with the author's opinion? Explain your answer.

_____

_____

_____

4. What is the theme or message of the story? Explain.

_____

_____

_____

R 3.4 Understand that *theme* refers to the meaning or moral of a selection and recognize themes (whether implied or stated directly) in sample works.

As you read *Weslandia*, fill in the Theme Chart.

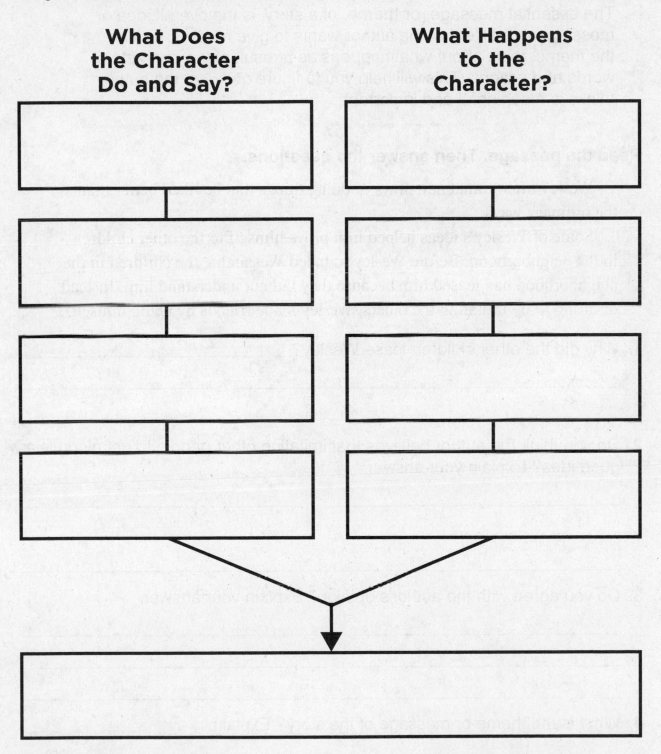

What Does the Character Do and Say?

What Happens to the Character?

How does the information you wrote in the Theme Chart help you make inferences and analyze *Weslandia*?

 R 3.4 Understand that *theme* refers to the meaning or moral of a selection and recognize themes (whether implied or stated directly) in sample works.

As I read, I will pay attention to intonation and phrasing.

	I handed in my Jupiter report today, but I don't remember
11	anything about the planet. That's because as soon as I got
22	home, excitement ruled. I could hear the noise about half a
33	mile away. When I got to the farm, there was bedlam!
44	"Well, if you didn't plant it, then how did it get here?"
56	I heard my mother yelling. My father said he didn't know how
68	the peculiar plant got there but that it had to be gotten rid of
82	right away. He didn't want our crop to be spoiled by some
94	mystery fruit.
96	"Hey, what's going on?" I asked over all the commotion.
106	"This!" shouted my mother as she pointed to a strange tree
117	in the middle of the orchard.
123	At first glance, when I looked at the tree, it looked like all
136	the other trees. But then I noticed the extraordinary fruit. Each
147	piece was round and yellow and had a big red spot on it. There
161	was just one spot, and each piece of fruit was the same. 173

Comprehension Check

1. What is the problem? **Problem and Solution**

2. Why does the father plan to get rid of the tree? **Main Idea and Details**

	Words Read	–	Number of Errors	=	Words Correct Score
First Read		–		=	
Second Read		–		=	

R 1.1 Read aloud narrative and expository text fluently and accurately
and with appropriate pacing, **intonation**, and expression.

Name _____

A **hyperlink** is an electronic connection within text on a Web page
that provides direct access to other documents or information.
A **key word** is a specific word that helps you find information.

**Look at the sample online encyclopedia entry. Then answer
the questions.**

| BACK | FORWARD | STOP | REFRESH | HOME | PRINT |

Address: http://www.example.com

Home | Browse | Newsletters | Favorites | Search | [   ] GO

> Living things that have parents that are quite different from each
> other are call <u>hybrids</u>. People sometimes breed hybrids because they
> may have more desirable traits than either of their parents. People often
> mate closely related living things on purpose. This process is called
> <u>crossbreeding</u>. A crossbreed is a product of mating individuals from
> two distinct breeds or varieties of the same <u>species</u>. Crossbreeding has
> given us new kinds of plants that resist disease, produce more food on
> the same area of land, and are more nutritious.

1. What are the hyperlinks on this page?

_____

2. If you wanted to find out about different cat breeds, where would you type
this information? What key words would you use?

_____

3. If you wanted more information about different species, which hyperlink
could you click on? How do you know?

_____

_____

R 2.1 Understand how text features (e.g., format, graphics, sequence,
diagrams, illustrations, charts, maps) make information accessible and
usable.

Name _____

The etymology, or **origin** of a word, can help you remember its definition. You can discover the origin of a word in a dictionary.

patio *n.* courtyard **[Sp]**

Find each of these words in the dictionary. Next to each word, tell from which language it comes.

1. city _____

2. ranch _____

3. athlete _____

4. spaghetti _____

5. samurai _____

6. rocket _____

7. guitar _____

8. kindergarten _____

9. tycoon _____

10. comrade _____

 R 1.2 Use word origins to determine the meaning of unknown words.

Name _____

Using the Word Study Steps

1. LOOK at the word.

2. SAY the word aloud.

3. STUDY the letters in the word.

4. WRITE the word.

5. CHECK the word.
Did you spell the word right?
If not, go back to step 1.

A. Find and Circle

Find and circle each of the spelling words in this puzzle. Words may read forward, backward, upward, downward, or diagonally.

```
E N B B E S N N K N C J K O T J T
U D P I I R R A R I O T G R I R E
N E E U S W Q A R O E S I S I T S
I L L P N E E T L X C P I C Y R R
F P L O I I C E F U L I Y N G I E
O I I Z Y T V T K E C C N E U A V
R R F M K I N E T L L O N U T N I
M T Y F I N U E R E Y N N R Q G N
E L C Y C I N U C S U T I I B L U
R E T E M I T N E C I P R L B E G
E L C Y C I B A L K O T I I C M R
C E N T U R Y Q B D D D Y B O O Q
```

B. List the words below as you find them in the puzzle.

1. _____   8. _____   15. _____

2. _____   9. _____   16. _____

3. _____   10. _____   17. _____

4. _____   11. _____   18. _____

5. _____   12. _____   19. _____

6. _____   13. _____   20. _____

7. _____   14. _____

CA **LC 1.5** Spell roots, suffixes, prefixes, contractions, and syllable constructions correctly.

Name _____

A. Circle the misspelled words in the passage. Write the words correctly on the lines below.

Jean-Pierre Blanchard and John Jefferies took one of the most daring trips of the sentury. They practiced biweeklie to make sure that everything went smoothly. The trip was going well until the temperature got colder, and they began to sink. "Help us!" they cried in unisun. To make the balloon lighter, Blanchard removed part of his unaform. Using his banoculars, Jefferies could see a small place to land. On the way down, they missed a tree branch by less than a centumeter.

1. _____   2. _____   3. _____

4. _____   5. _____   6. _____

B. Writing Activity

Write a paragraph about where you would go if you had a chance to ride in a hot-air balloon. Use four words from your spelling list.

_____

_____

_____

_____

_____

_____

_____

_____

_____

_____

_____

LC 1.5 Spell roots, suffixes, prefixes, contractions, and syllable constructions correctly.

Name _____

- A **prepositional phrase** is a group of words that begins with a preposition and ends with a noun or pronoun.
- A prepositional phrase makes a connection between two nouns or pronouns in a sentence.
- The **object** of a preposition is the noun or pronoun that follows the preposition.

A. Underline the preposition in each sentence. Circle the object of the preposition.

1. Jacques Charles learned about hydrogen.

2. They waved from the balloon.

3. Balloonists cannot be afraid of heights.

4. François Pilâtre De Rozier anchored his balloon with a tether.

5. The first human passenger flew over Paris.

B. Complete each sentence with a prepositional phrase.

6. The wind was strong _____ that they left.

7. There were 25 members _____.

8. A duck, a rooster, and a sheep rode _____.

9. _____, the balloonists prepared to launch.

10. The balloons _____ were a beautiful sight.

LC 1.1 Identify and correctly use **prepositional phrases**, appositives, and independent and dependent clauses; use transitions and conjunctions to connect ideas.

© Macmillan/McGraw-Hill

Name _____

Read the paragraph below. Rewrite the paragraph correctly on the lines provided. Be sure to add commas where needed and to remove incorrect commas. Replace any prepositions that are used incorrectly.

From her balloon perch Cynthia looked at the world laid out beneath her. The trees reached from her as though to tickle the balloon basket as she passed. The lakes and rivers sparkled and winked on the sun. The green above the grass looked brighter than Cynthia had ever thought it could. She gave a sigh to contentment. She wished that she could stay about her balloon, forever.

_____

_____

_____

_____

_____

_____

_____

_____

_____

_____

_____

_____

_____

_____

_____

_____

_____

LC 1.1 Identify and correctly use **prepositional phrases**, appositives, and independent and dependent clauses; use transitions and conjunctions to connect ideas.

Name _____

1. For each of the following sentences, CIRCLE the subject and
UNDERLINE the predicate. The first two are done for you.

Examples:

During class, (she) checked out the teacher's shoes.

After she tripped, (he) fell down laughing.

Now, you:

After lunch, Jake darted to the door.

Over the weekend, Caitlin raised $30 for the school fund-raiser.

2. Open your journal to the entry on when you were part of a successful
team. (If you don't have that one, choose the one before it.)

3. Choose two sentences from that entry and write them below.

4. For each of the sentences, CIRCLE the subject and UNDERLINE
the predicate.

_____

_____

_____

_____

_____

_____

CA **W 1.0** Writing Strategies

Name _____

Some words end with **-able** or **-ible**. When they are added as suffixes, they change the word's meaning. Both of these suffixes mean "able to be," "capable of being," "likely to," "worthy of being," "fit for," or "tending to."

A. Think about adding -able or -ible to complete each word. Write the complete word on the line at the right.

1. cap____   _____

2. invis____   _____

3. poss____   _____

4. us____   _____

5. suit____   _____

B. Add the suffix -able or -ible to create a new word. Write the new word on the line. Then write a sentence containing that word.

6. break   _____

_____

7. sense   _____

_____

8. convert   _____

_____

9. honor   _____

_____

10. collapse   _____

_____

Name _____

| attraction | emerged | inquire | focused |

A. Replace the underlined word or words in each sentence with a vocabulary word from the box.

1. We <u>concentrated</u> on the waves and nothing else, hoping to see a whale.

   _____

2. The immense blue whale finally <u>rose into view</u> from the water.

   _____

3. If you <u>ask</u> at the library, the librarians can provide several books about whales. _____

4. The beautiful harbor was the town's greatest <u>draw</u> for tourists.

   _____

B. Read each sentence below. Choose the correct meaning of the underlined word. Circle the letter of your answer.

5. The villagers had many <u>discussions</u> before they decided on a plan.

   a. conversations   **b.** problems   **c.** parties

6. The sleeping adult seals were <u>sprawled</u> across the beach as their pups played in the surf.

   a. in motion   **b.** awake and watchful   **c.** lying with limbs spread out

7. When she was frightened, the young child became <u>unreasonable</u> and wouldn't listen to her parents.

   a. foolish and senseless   **b.** happy and cheerful   **c.** easily distracted

8. After the scientists assured them that it was safe to do so, they <u>ventured</u> to touch the whale.

   a. feared   **b.** dared   **c.** planned

© Macmillan/McGraw-Hill

 R 1.0 Word Analysis, Fluency, and Systematic Vocabulary Development

When you summarize, you tell the most important events, ideas, and details of a story or a text.

Read the story. Answer the question that follows each paragraph.

When I was younger, I was very shy. I dreamed of becoming an actor, but I couldn't imagine ever performing in front of others. My mother I always told me "Alma, dreams come true for people who make them come true."

1. What is Alma's problem? _____

_____

For my tenth birthday, I decided to follow my mother's advice. I asked my parents if I could enroll in acting lessons. My parents agreed and signed me up for lessons with Mrs. Parker, an acting coach in our community.

2. What does Alma do to solve her problem? _____

_____

When my mother dropped me off at Mrs. Parker's house, I was so terrified I could hardly say hello. Mrs. Parker put me at ease, though. Soon we were doing a few simple acting exercises. Before long, I forgot my shyness as I learned to put my heart and mind into different characters.

3. What happens at Mrs. Parker's house? _____

_____

I knew I had overcome my shyness once and for all when I gathered the courage to audition for the school play. I didn't get the lead role, but I did get a supporting role. I plan to audition for more plays. If I keep working hard and practicing, maybe one day you'll see me, Alma Sanchez, on the big screen.

4. How does the story end? _____

_____

R 3.2 Identify the main problem or conflict of the plot and explain how it is resolved.

The Gri Gri Tree • **Grade 5/Unit 6**   **365**

As you read *The Gri Gri Tree*, fill in the Summarize Chart.

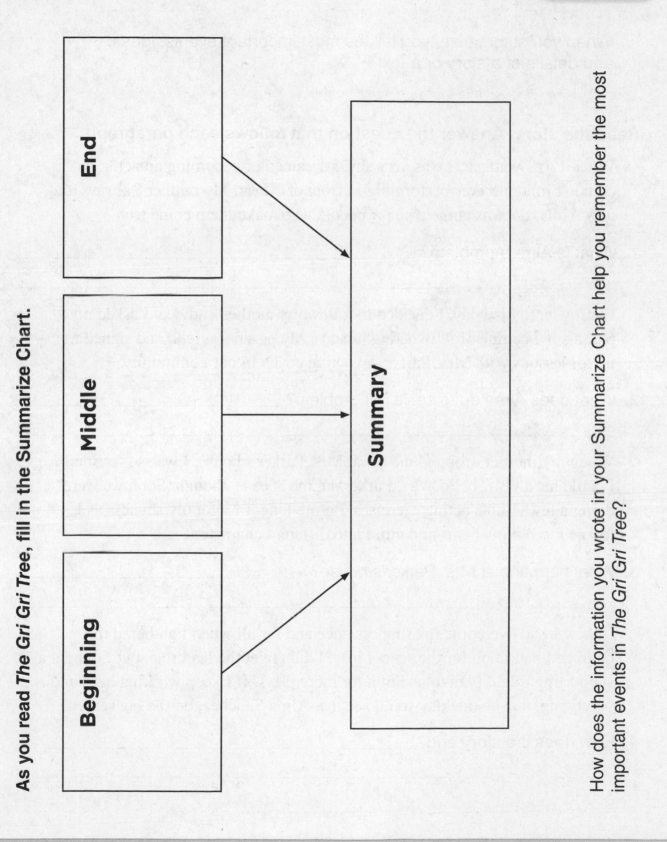

Beginning	Middle	End

Summary

How does the information you wrote in your Summarize Chart help you remember the most important events in *The Gri Gri Tree*?

CA **R 3.2** Identify the main problem or conflict of the plot and explain how it is resolved.

Name _____

As I read, I will pay attention to pacing.

	"Hurry up!" Caitlin said to her brother Domenic.
8	Domenic was loaded down with his toolbox and some
17	lumber. "I'm walking as fast as I can!" he said. "Besides,
28	we've got all day tomorrow to work on the decorations.
38	What's the hurry?"
41	It was Friday afternoon, and Caitlin and Domenic were on
51	their way to their grandmother's house. First thing Saturday
60	morning, they would get busy decorating Grandma's
67	basement. They were having a big family party there on
77	Sunday afternoon.
79	Domenic had been studying about the ocean animals
87	that live on a coral reef. He and Caitlin had decided to turn
100	Grandma's basement into an undersea world. Caitlin had
108	already sketched the cardboard fish that she would hang
117	from the ceiling. Domenic planned to build a treasure chest.
127	Then he and Caitlin would fill it with prizes.
136	"What a terrific idea!" Grandma said when she heard
145	their plans. "I'll help with the decorations too and I . . . ."
155	Grandma's voice trailed off. Her eyes were twinkling.
163	That always happened when she had a truly great idea. 173

Comprehension Check

1. How did Domenic and Caitlin come up with the theme for decorating Grandma's basement? **Main Idea and Details**

2. What do you think Grandma's idea is? **Plot Development**

	Words Read	−	Number of Errors	=	Words Correct Score
First Read		−		=	
Second Read		−		=	

 R 1.1 Read aloud narrative and expository text fluently and accurately and with appropriate **pacing**, intonation, and expression.

Name _____

A line **graph** shows how data changes over time.

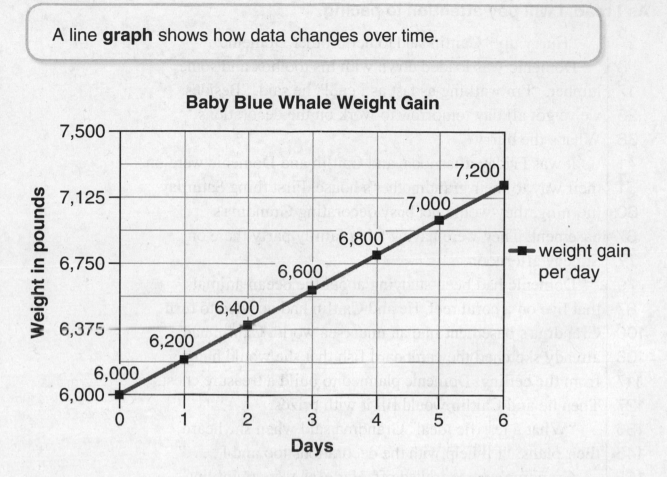

Baby Blue Whale Weight Gain

The graph above shows the weight gain of the blue whales for one week. Use the graph to answer the questions below.

1. What is the title of this graph?

_____

2. How much does the blue whale weigh on the first day?

_____

3. How much weight does a blue whale gain per day? _____

4. How much will a blue whale weigh on day 7? How did you get your answer?

_____

_____

_____

© Macmillan/McGraw-Hill

R 2.1 Understand how text features (e.g., format, graphics, sequence, diagrams, illustrations, charts, maps) make information accessible and usable.

Name _____

A word root is part of a word that does not usually stand by itself as a base word. Prefixes or suffixes are attached to a word root. Many word roots are Latin in origin. If you know the meaning of the **Latin root**, you can figure out the meaning of an unfamiliar word.

Read each sentence. Write the meaning of each boldface word on the line provided. Use the table of Latin roots below to help you determine each definition.

Root	Meaning
duct	lead, take, bring
medius	middle
fortis	strong
tract	pull or draw

1. Does water **contract** or expand when it freezes? _____

_____

2. The boys could not agree, so a **mediator** was called in to hear both

arguments. _____

_____

3. The **aqueducts** brought water into the ancient city. _____

_____

4. Let's make a **deduction** based on the facts we know. _____

_____

5. The troops **fortified** the town in preparation for the enemy invasion.

_____

R 1.4 Know abstract, derived roots and affixes from Greek and Latin and use this knowledge to analyze the meaning of complex words (e.g., *controversial*).

Name _____

Using the Word Study Steps

1. LOOK at the word.

2. SAY the word aloud.

3. STUDY the letters in the word.

4. WRITE the word.

5. CHECK the word.
   Did you spell the word right?
   If not, go back to step 1.

A. Fill-Ins

Fill in the missing letters of each word to form a spelling word.

1. collaps ___ ___ ___ e

2. break ___ ___ ___ e

3. afford ___ ___ ___ e

4. us ___ ___ ___ e

5. bear ___ ___ ___ e

6. favor ___ ___ ___ e

7. cap ___ ___ l ___

8. enjoy ___ ___ ___ ___ ___

9. honor ___ ___ ___ e

10. convert ___ ___ ___ e

11. invis ___ ___ l ___

12. unreason ___ ___ l ___

13. respect ___ ___ ___ e

14. sens ___ ___ l ___

15. unbeliev ___ ___ ___ e

16. poss ___ ___ l ___

17. suit ___ ___ ___ e

18. laugh ___ ___ ___ ___

19. lik ___ ___ ___ ___

20. comfort ___ ___ ___ ___

B. Alphabetical Order

Use the lines below to write the spelling words in alphabetical order.

1. _____   6. _____   11. _____   16. _____

2. _____   7. _____   12. _____   17. _____

3. _____   8. _____   13. _____   18. _____

4. _____   9. _____   14. _____   19. _____

5. _____   10. _____   15. _____   20. _____

 LC 1.5 Spell roots, suffixes, prefixes, contractions, and syllable constructions correctly.

Name _____

A. Circle the misspelled words in the passage. Write the words correctly on the lines provided.

    Welcome to the Hawaii Science College! We do our best to make getting a science degree affordible for everyone. You will find the cost of our classes is not unreasonble. Also, we want your time here as a student to be enjoyabl. Our teachers are likeble people who will help you meet the challenge of college-level homework. With a degree from our school, anything is possable! So let's start the tour. Please let me know whether we can do anything to make your visit here more comfortible.

1. _____   2. _____   3. _____

4. _____   5. _____   6. _____

B. Writing Activity

Write a paragraph about your favorite outdoor activity or school subject. Use four words from your spelling list.

_____

_____

_____

_____

_____

_____

_____

_____

_____

_____

_____

CA LC 1.5 Spell roots, suffixes, prefixes, contractions, and syllable constructions correctly.

Name _____

> • You can combine two sentences that tell about the same noun by adding an **adjective** to one of the sentences.
> • You can combine two sentences that tell about the same action by adding an **adverb** to one sentence.
> • You can also combine two sentences that tell about the same location by adding a **prepositional phrase** to one sentence.

Read each pair of sentences. Combine them with an adjective, an adverb, or a prepositional phrase.

1. Dennis walked to a pond. The pond was small.

_____

2. He worked in the lab. It was a science lab.

_____

3. He went to college. The college was in Seattle.

_____

4. Dennis helped others. He helped them happily.

_____

5. The scientists traveled to a camp. It was a mountain camp.

_____

6. Rivers were flooded by mud. They were flooded quickly.

_____

7. The helicopter flew over the blast zone. It flew low.

_____

8. Dennis found living things. He found them in the lakes.

_____

 LC 1.0 Written and Oral English Language Conventions

Name _____

Read the paragraph below. Rewrite the paragraph, combining short sentences that deal with the same subject and correcting punctuation.

dennis went to school He went to school to become a scientist. scientists study. They study nature Dennis knew that he would like to be a scientist. He knew because he liked to study nature. he learned how to dive. He learned in order to study ocean plants. One day he flew in a helicopter. He flew in one and collected water samples These samples helped scientists learn. They helped scientists learn about how living things survive. do you think science is important Study nature as Dennis did. Go to school like dennis did. Then you can become a scientist, too

_____

_____

_____

_____

_____

_____

_____

_____

_____

_____

_____

_____

Name _____

1. Remember earlier in the unit, we rewrote sentences by just rearranging the order.

2. Note that today, we are also going to rewrite sentences by:

   1. rearranging the order

      AND in addition, we are going to:

   2. use our knowledge of subjects and predicates to divide the sentences into parts

3. Read the following sentence.

   Edgar ate the eggs even though he hated them.

4. Circle the subject and underline the predicate.

5. Rewrite the sentence below by rearranging the subject and predicate (often called the "components" of a sentence).

Example: Even though he hated them, Edgar ate the eggs.

6. Now circle the subject and underline the predicate to check to see that you did rearrange the components. Note: The new sentence is not always a "better" sentence. It's just different and gives you some choices when you are writing and rewriting.

7. Now, for each of the following sentences:

   A. Circle the subject, and underline the predicate AND

   B. Use the space below the sentence to reorder the components.

   i. My cousin Demitris plays squash every afternoon at 2:45.

   Reorder: _____

   _____

   ii. The fourteen-pound tomato was the winner of the produce contest.

   Reorder: _____

   _____

   iii. I mow the lawn at home twice a month.

   Reorder: _____

   _____

© Macmillan/McGraw-Hill

CA W 1.0 Writing Strategies

Making inferences can help you trace the plot development of a story. You make inferences when you use clues in the story and your own knowledge to figure out information about characters and events that are not directly stated in the story.

Read each passage, then make an inference about the situations and characters.

1. Bob Lemmons saw the wild mustangs and pulled the reins to slow his horse, Warrior. The mustangs looked up but didn't run.
Inference: Bob slowed his horse because

_____

2. Bob was the only cowboy who could get close to the wild horses. They accepted him into the herd.
Inference: Bob's relationship with horses was

_____

3. The sky darkened, and Bob saw lightning flash around him. He quickly led Warrior to a ravine for shelter.
Inference: Bob and Warrior sought shelter because

_____

4. The mustang stallion fought Bob and Warrior. Bob guided Warrior's blows and the stallion fell, returning meekly to the herd.
Inference: The leaders of the mustang herd after the fight are

_____

5. Analyze your inferences. What do they tell you about Bob's life as a

cowboy? _____

_____

_____

CA **R 2.4** Draw inferences, conclusions, or generalizations about text and support them with textual evidence and prior knowledge.